The Stillwater Buckskin

Discover the transforming power of ancient wisdom…

This addition to your management library
is presented with my thanks. Your contribution
to our success is appreciated. The story
illustrates and reinforces our belief that character
and integrity are never out of style.

Brad Buckles

The
Stillwater
Buckskin

Discover the transforming power of ancient wisdom…

Kim A. Nelson

This book is dedicated to
my wife, the finest person I know,
with a note of silent gratitude to the late
Joseph Kibitony,
friend and singer of songs.

Acknowledgment

A special acknowledgement to those who made the book possible:

Don Pugh, an honest and trustworthy friend.

Jane Pugh, whose heart is a spring of pure sweet water

Steve Robinson, fly-fisherman and true believer.

Cary Wasden, a Thomas Jefferson in progress.

John Steffens, both master carpenter and master human being.

Thanks also to the Joseph Thunderbulls in my life, named and unnamed, whose friendship and wisdom make it, with all its ups and downs, so joyful! I would like to thank those who contributed time and talent to encourage this endeavor in particular: Craig Nelson, Ben Marra, Connie Day, Hank Skidmore, Andy Skinner, Dan Hogan, JD Field, Gordon and Myrna Conger, Debbie Calhoun, Emily Watts, Rachel Johnson, Chanda Hair, Galen Hunt, Bill Phillips, and so many more.

Finally, special thanks to my daughters, son-in-law, and grandchildren—the real reason the future matters so much.

Contents

Chapter One

The Wisdom of
Joseph Thunderbull

~~~≈≈≈≈~~~

All The People belong to you,
and you belong to all The People.

To help them is to help you,
and to hurt them is to hurt you.

✠

The Stillwater Buckskin

The time has come to share the story of Joseph Thunderbull. Over the last 30 plus years, I have used the wisdom my friend and mentor gave me to build a wonderful life and a very successful corporation. With the help of what I have learned I have found the balance that gives my life peace and joy. Though I have shared some of what I had been given with others in order to help them grow into who they knew in their hearts they could be, they have had only a portion of the feast that is available.

The reason to tell the story now is that people may listen. We have always needed it but the times have been too good for us to hear. It has been too easy for us. In the case of teaching hard and worthwhile lessons to people, timing is everything. I received this wisdom from my friend and mentor Joseph Thunderbull, as he taught me what his grandfather had taught him.

We sat in front of a warm pot-bellied stove in a cave in the Rocky Mountains during the first blizzard of the year. It was here Joseph taught me the power of preparation and timing in effective teaching. We talked of the old way of passing on learning by recounting the wisdom of the People. He introduced me to the impact of difficulty as a motivator for change. Joseph, ever the consummate teacher, taught me about the attention-getting power of winter and want with a storm howling its confirmation only a few feet away. Here is what he said:

"When the People are warm and filled in the summer, it is the oldest men and women who make the most medicine for good hunting. The more cold winters they have known, the wiser they become about the use of the summer and autumn harvest seasons.

"The People grow complacent with full bellies and warm nights. It is only when the wolf howls close by that we look for our weapons in earnest. Real learning is not without a price. The personal pride and greed of easy winters is lost only when the cold comes that demands every person's warmth for survival.

"It is not a mistake that the time we gather to hear old ones tell the learning stories is in the winter. Empty bellies have open ears. The darkest, coldest nights open the hardest and most selfish hearts. The starving moon is when the summer work and autumn harvest seem most important."

I had come to believe that we needed to hear the wolves before we would be willing to open our ears and listen to the words of the wise ones. The wolves are howling in the world now and the people may be ready.

Joseph had given me all he had, without any concern for what he might receive in return. The principles he had shared were beyond price, but that was not his greatest gift to me. Joseph Thunderbull had given me a more valuable gift by far. He had given me his trust, and that was a sacred thing. He had taught me trust and love for self and others: I could not shirk the responsibility of that teaching.

Not long ago, I sat facing a beautiful spring day in our New York branch office. The windows of the 40th floor revealed a fair view of the city. However, the view of the future was not so clear. The reservoir of my emotional strength was being tested. Many friends had been lost in the attack on the World Trade Center. And in the six months that followed, colleagues I had grown to respect as leaders in business seemed bound for prison as mounting concerns over unethical practices came to light. The world seemed to be a dark and hopeless place for many people.

I believed that part of the feeling of hopelessness in the business community came from a fear that our business model was somehow inherently flawed. I also felt we were looking for the causes of our deteriorating condition in the wrong place. We seemed to be asking how to regulate economic health back into our world. We were looking at the system for flaws, when I knew we should have been looking in the mirror.

I decided a book would be the best way to share what I had come to know as the wisdom of the Stillwater Buckskin. The problem I faced was, who could I find to write the story in the way it deserved to be written? That skill was not a gift I possessed, but the story needed to be written so others could benefit.

If I was going to invite people to change their lives, I must find a writer capable of bringing the power of the buckskin alive. Joseph had often quoted the old Zen wisdom that says when the student is ready, the teacher will appear. I had been looking for a person gifted enough to share the story and message of Joseph Thunderbull effectively. This person would need talent as a writer, a willingness to learn, and a good heart. As I contemplated who could bring the story to life, Jane Hogan called on the phone. This coincidence was not to be ignored. Jane was a respected and seasoned business journalist as well as a friend.

I had first met Jane at a party when I was a sophomore in college. She was a freshman attending Columbia University's School of Journalism. She had been a high school friend of my future wife and then girlfriend,

Rebecca. Rebecca had spotted her at the party and introduced us. That chance meeting had led to occasional social contact and some very interesting business and political discussions throughout our undergraduate years. She was bright, enthusiastic, positive, and idealistic. I entered graduate school, we both started careers, and, although we had continued communication at business and academic conferences socially, we drifted apart.

I was in my mid-30s before I allowed the impact of Joseph and the Stillwater Buckskin to change my life. I knew—or at least believed—it could do the same for others. When I first thought of telling the story, I was starting a new business and reintroducing myself to my wife and kids. Sharing the lessons Joseph had taught me with the world at large would have to wait. Actually, I should admit I was not confident enough at that time to know if I was capable of judging the value of what I had learned. I decided to test it in my own life before announcing to the world I had a great message.

I started at that moment to apply one of the first lessons Joseph had taught me: I would pay attention to the job at hand. His motto was simple: Observe, evaluate, and act. That began my preparation for success. I would pay attention. I would find a way to contribute to the success of every project I participated in and every person I met. The Stillwater Buckskin would wait. I would know when to share its principles and the other lessons Joseph had taught. Shaman and mentor Joseph Thunderbull was fond of reminding me that every season has its own purpose. Trying to harvest before you plant is like confusing motion with production. No matter how hard you appear to be working, you don't get much done. Preparation makes the harvest possible.

A purposeful journey requires two things. First, you must know where you are. Second, you must know where you are going. Joseph said that is why all the maps in shopping malls have those little arrows that say "You are here." You need to know where you are before you start, and you need to know where you want to go to be sure you go in the right direction. I needed to plant before I could harvest, so I let the message wait.

Then the time came to share the story. Was Jane the one to write it? After a journalism degree and some experience, Jane had returned to school for an MBA. It became clear to her that she would specialize in business writing, and she was nothing if not committed to being the best. She wrote her thesis on ethics in business. This work had focused on the impact corporate ethics had on the lives of the people it touched, its suppliers, clients, and their families.

Was the enthusiastic, idealistic, hopeful Jane I had known still in the heart of the seasoned and skeptical professional journalist she had become? Had her association with journalism's elite over the years hardened or perhaps just jaded her professionally? She had recently written a prize-winning book on the state of American business and the potential fall of global capitalism. She was and always had been a top-notch writer. However, it seemed to me that as time passed her writing had become increasingly pessimistic. I was very discouraged about her outlook after reading her last column on the flaws of the system. She seemed pessimistic, but knew that for many companies the system still worked. She wanted to know why it worked for some but not all. We had discussed possibilities many times. Our company was a fly in her philosophical ointment, our success an itch she could not scratch. I think in her heart she still wanted to believe in the American dream, in spite of recent events that suggested a basic flaw in the integrity of the corporate system.

She knew I believed corporate integrity and success were not mutually exclusive. In fact, she had heard me say on more than one occasion that I had come to believe that long-term success and corporate integrity were inseparable. Bits and pieces of how I had come by my management and interpersonal philosophies had surfaced as we had talked. Our people and our clients were happy, committed, and successful. She always seemed curious and interested about that. Her position seemed to be that people were generally losing confidence in the economic and social future. Many were asking if the free market system was doomed.

As I reflected on whether Jane should be the one to tell the story, I wondered if there was enough spark of the old optimism left to help her rekindle her belief in the future.

"Times change but people don't" were the words Joseph Thunderbull had spoken in response to a claim that society was doomed. A fellow steelworker pronouncing doom one day in 1969 claimed the changing world environment had made the current generation futureless. All was hopeless for them. Looking back, it was now clear that somehow we had made it. Many had even prospered. The old Indian had been right. That was over 30 years ago. It was Vietnam, Watergate, the oil embargo, and 9/11 ago.

Could we be successful now? Was it possible to be happy and peaceful now? Joseph was right in 1969, and even though the times had changed people hadn't. We had within us the capacity not just for success but greatness. We had it then and we have it now. More than a century before I heard the words of Joseph Thunderbull, Abraham Lincoln had stood on the verge of a horrible war that threatened his beloved republic. Lincoln had said in response to the hopeless feelings of his fellows, "People are just about as happy as they make up their minds to be." President Lincoln knew we participated fully in determining the quality of our lives.

It was unquestionably the right time for me to share the wisdom of Joseph Thunderbull. I had read Kicking Bird's words from the Stillwater Buckskin every day for many years. I would take a week to consider how to deliver that wisdom most effectively. I would go to the mountains and think it through. It would be good to be in the Stillwater again. Rebecca and I left the following day. Two weeks later I called Jane Hogan to ask if she was interested in telling the story. She had heard me speak of my friend Joseph many times and knew I respected him. We talked for quite some time. I shared briefly what I thought the scope and purpose of the project would be.

When I was finished she asked two questions: "Why have you finally decided to share such a personal story?" and "Why did you choose me to write it?" My answers were simple and came without any hesitation.

"I want to tell the story to help others appreciate the opportunity for success, joy, and wisdom life still offers. I want you to write it for one reason: after knowing your heart and reading your work, talking to those you have worked for and with, I can't get one thought out of my mind—my friend Joseph Thunderbull would have liked you . . . and you would have liked him a lot. I believe it will affect you as it has me. You have a special gift that will allow others to be touched by it as well."

There was a brief pause . . . "When do we start?" she asked.

We arranged to meet a week later in my office.

Jane took a comfortable chair, placed a yellow legal pad in her lap, and started the small recorder that sat on the table between us. Our meeting started simply. "Jane," I said, "it may just be chance that brings us together to work on this project, but I don't think so.

"Much of what I am and what I have accomplished I owe to a chance meeting more than 30 years ago. That is where I will begin."

Chapter Two

Meeting
Joseph Thunderbull

———〰〰〰———

The purpose of this life is to love and learn;
this is how you must spend your time.

✦

The Stillwater Buckskin

"Times change but people don't." It was the first thing I ever heard the old Indian say. His name was Joseph Thunderbull. I had been working as a laborer on a high-rise construction site for about a month. I was 18 and new to the trades. My father knew the owner of the construction company and had arranged a well-paying job for me the summer before my freshman year in college.

I remember my father's parting comment, "I can get you a job, but only you can keep it." I needed the job and I knew my father well enough to know that he wasn't kidding. I had, no doubt, been hired with instructions to fire me if I didn't turn out to be a great hand. I worked hard and tried to fit in.

Just "fitting in" was what I was doing on that June day so many years ago when I heard Joseph speak for the first time. The guys on the crew had been talking about the usual stuff—the uselessness of the federal government and of course "know-nothing" architects. They had designed this building yet couldn't build a doghouse without the help of "real men"—meaning us. The older hands discussed the litany of things that were going to hell in a hand basket. The basket must have been huge given all the things that were going to hell in it.

I was sitting on a pile of structural steel eating my lunch with the crew. Joseph was sitting about 12 feet straight in front of me on another pile, reading a book as he ate his lunch with apparently little interest in what was being said. I was listening intently to the conversation, although not actively participating.

One iron worker, a huge capable man we all feared, had just made a global pronouncement of great import:

"The kids today are all going to hell in a hand basket. The world has changed so much there is no chance for these kids to learn a thing. They don't value or respect anything. They refuse to learn how to work. They are all worthless, long-haired, commie-loving, TV junkies." He paused and delivered his dramatic summary: "The world is doomed." I joined the general head nodding of the crowd, forgetting for a moment that I was barely 18 years old.

As we sat digesting his comments the old Indian sitting across from me spoke. "Times change but people don't," he said. "These kids will find a way to figure it out." He looked at me thoughtfully, and then went on eating his lunch and reading his book. He was clearly a man of few words and had just said all he wanted to say. What impressed me was that no one, including the big man who had just finished "the world is doomed speech," took exception to the words of the old carpenter. In fact, they all acted as if not only did he know what he was talking about but his word was beyond challenge. His comments acted as the closing bell for lunch. Without a word everyone put away his lunch and returned to work. I was stunned—and incredibly curious.

It was clear to me the construction workers respected him, and I wanted to know why.

For the remainder of the week I paid special attention to the old Indian while I was at work. On the following Monday morning the foreman gave me the usual in-depth direction, his attention to detail befitting my lofty station on the crew: He told me to "report to Joe." Up to that point I did not even know his name. I learned later that his name was Joseph Thunderbull, and he preferred

Joseph to Joe. I reported to Joseph every morning from that day until I left for college in September. I didn't know it at the time, but Joseph Thunderbull was to be both a mentor and a friend. It was a relationship that would change my life. He would teach me to observe things as they were and learn from everything and everyone around me. He helped me look beyond the obvious and bridge the gap to what lay beyond.

I embarked that morning on a wonderful journey. In fact, looking back, that morning changed me forever. I remember remarking to a colleague years later that I was one of a few students in the history of education to get PhD-equivalent schooling in wisdom and character outside the classroom; it started for me that summer when the foreman assigned me to "report to Joe."

Joseph became my professor, classmate, and advisor. The classroom was an urban construction site, a farmhouse at the edge of the city, and several remote Rocky Mountain valleys. The degree was a doctorate of interest, a sort of PhD of learning.

The first morning when I reported to Joseph he looked at me stoically. His brown eyes were the only part of his face that was smiling, which is, as I recall him, how they almost always were. Joseph looked me over and said, "The guys say you are a rich kid." I had, of course, heard this before. The comment was a reference, no doubt, to the fact that my father played golf with the company owner, was financially successful, and had arranged for my job.

Joseph then asked me in rapid succession how much money I had in the bank, if I owned a business or building, and how many employees I had.

I answered, "130 bucks, no, and zero."

"Just as I suspected," he chuckled. "You're not a rich kid. You're a rich kid's kid. I'll straighten the boys out later," he said. "We wouldn't want them wrong on such important facts. Well, we know who your daddy is, but we don't know who you are. So, let's find out."

He threw me a safety belt and we went to work. He had sized me up in a moment. His challenge provided me the simplest and most powerful spark possible. I set out from that moment to be somebody. It was clear to me that Joseph would judge me by my work, not by who someone else thought I might be or by who my father was.

As we worked, it became evident to me why the other tradesmen respected Joseph. He was amazing—never a wasted step or movement. He was never without the right tool or in the wrong place. This example began my education. His mantra for the jobsite, for the rest of life, I was to learn, was as simple as it was effective: observe, evaluate, act.

"Make it a habit in all you do," he said. "It applies at all times and in all places. Before you do anything, learn as much as you can about it. Think about what it is you choose to do. Evaluate what impact your action will have, and then do it. Most people don't have the patience to do all three. Some people want to observe forever. Others want to evaluate things to death until there is no risk. Still others simply want to get it done. I guess it hasn't occurred to them to make sure they know what 'it' is and how to 'get it done' before they start doing it. That is why you will see a guy cutting the steel for the same connection three times, because the first two cuts didn't fit.

"Remember, Bill," he taught, "the old wisdom is true—it is better to measure twice and cut only once. Notice how committed the nonplanners are to speed as they run to the gang box four times for tools they should have had, or run to the phone to order some new saw blades. 'I was sure I had one of these in the truck,' you can hear them say. They have confused motion with production.

"However, the most common problem among those who fail is that they fail to act at all. They would rather do nothing than risk anything. They forget that doing nothing gets nothing done. There is always some risk in any worthy endeavor. The trick is to do your homework and make that risk as small as possible.

"Find out what needs to be done, figure out the best way, and then do it. If you see someone with a better idea, use it. Give credit, say thanks, but use it.

"Observe," he would say. "Always observe. It's like Yogi Berra said, 'You can see a lot by just lookin.'"

Again and again I heard, "Observe, evaluate, and act. The devil is in the details."

Joseph always carried a short pencil and a small spiral notebook in his shirt pocket for noting what he saw or jotting down a thought. He said getting those small pencils was the only good reason he ever found for golf. "No one can remember all the things of value that come and go in a day without writing some notes. Our minds are always working," he told me, "and there is no telling when it might come up with the solution to a problem you have been considering. Sometimes when you are working or even sleeping your conscious mind gets out of the way and inspiration can happen. When this happens I make a note so I will not loose what I have been given.

"My Grandfather taught me to listen for the wisdom of others. When I hear a thought that is new to me I will make a note of it. That way I will have it later when I am able to take the time to consider it. I have collected many such thoughts over the years. I am amazed at the wealth of wisdom available if we just pay attention. So I carry this small book and as I observe I note what I want to remember. Later after I consider it, I see if there is not some way for me to use what I have learned."

The first two months of working together passed quickly. I learned how to work, not just the frantic pace that I had always thought was real work, but the methodical, ground-eating, sustainable pace of a master. I can't tell you how many times I heard Joseph say, "Don't confuse motion and production." Joseph knew process was only as valuable as the product.

Don't get me wrong—by the end of every day I was dog-tired. The miracle of combining preparation and consistent purposeful effort was how much we got done and the effortless appearance of it. Joseph taught me how much of success was preparation and planning by showing me. He never forgot the doing though. He said that half of many people's lives was making "to do" lists. The other half was copying the same thing onto a new list the next day.

"Never forget when you put it on your list," he would say. "In order for something to get done, someone must do something."

He was always the first one there in the morning. To lay out his day, he said. I think he just loved the morning. On top of that he loved the feel of being prepared and doing a job right.

We were finishing up one Thursday when I received the first real compliment Joseph ever gave me. He said he was building a fence as a favor for the old couple he lived with and needed a hand to help. He asked if I was interested. I looked around for another hand to make sure he was talking to me. I was the only other person there. I told him I would be happy to help. He didn't look up from the cord he was coiling.

"Thanks," he said. "I'll give you the directions tomorrow."

His apartment was the basement of a small family farm home on the edge of the city. The couple who lived there was older and childless, and they welcomed his company and help around the place. He had lived there off and on for almost 20 years. He went home to the mountains whenever the urge struck him, and returned to work in the city whenever that seemed like the right thing to do. This had been the general way of his life since the death of his wife and young son 20 years earlier. When he was in town, the basement was where he lived.

When he referred to home—where he was from—he called it "the Stillwater." He spoke the term with a reverence that left me undecided if the Stillwater was indeed a place or a state of being. What was clear in either case was his respect for his home. In time I learned that the Stillwater was in fact a region, the place of his birth and rearing. His grandmother and grandfather were buried there. His younger sister, Sarah, lived there with her two young sons. I would come to love the Stillwater of Joseph Thunderbull both as a place and a state of being. I still go there when I need to find the unique peace of this world as well as peace of mind.

Building the fence along the back of the old couple's property was my first reason to visit Joseph at his "city house," as he referred to it. The couple who owned the house kept a single milk cow, and she was fond of the greener pastures the time-worn back fence offered. The fence had been patched so many times, according to Joseph, there was nothing left substantial enough to tie into. Repair could not make it sound—it had to be rebuilt.

Joseph was always teaching. He told me that the poem "Good Fences Make Good Neighbors" could be about boundaries, as he had once read in an old college literature text, but there was much more.

"Building anything to last and for a good purpose helps build good people. Teaching a person why he is working is as important as teaching him how to work," he said. "Such work is a lesson to others about the quality of person you are and the quality of people they could be."

"So why are we building this fence?" I asked.

I never knew what to expect when I asked Joseph such an open and philosophically inviting question, although the answer usually came in one of two categories. The first was the abrupt "Don't question the master" type answer. This was the kind Mr. Miagi gave to Daniel-san in the *Karate Kid* movies when Daniel asked how waxing a car or painting would help him learn to fight. I came to call these his "wax on, wax off" responses. The gist of these answers was always the same: be patient, observe, and when the time is right you will learn.

The second was the spiritual, philosophical, and sometimes very complex answer. These answers, or discussions actually, were always enjoyable. Joseph encouraged comment, question, challenge, or all three. Joseph referred to discussion as the backbone of civilization. He said for centuries such exchanges between student and professor, holy man and pilgrim, mother and child, leader and follower, coach and player were the very fabric of learning.

"No matter who the participants, or what the setting," he asserted, "the process became students learning together."

I came to refer to these discussion answers as "school."

There was one other general category of response from Joseph, although sometimes he did not require a question to be asked for one of these moments to occur. These were the rare times when Joseph would drag out his soapbox, then get up on it and preach. These pronouncements were offered without invitation or inclination toward discussion. They could be formal and were most often reverential. They were Native American council fire oratory, according to Joseph Thunderbull—the expressions of core beliefs, proven policy, and wisdom. There was no need for discussion. These were the objects in the universe that didn't move with or without discussion. In these moments, I referred to Joseph as "going Indian."

"So why are we building this fence?" I had asked.

After a brief introspective pause, he looked into my questioning face and said, "So the cow won't get out." Wax on, wax off . . . and we went to work.

We worked all day Saturday and finished the fence just as it was getting dark. It would have taken most two-man teams at least two days to build that fence. We were able to do it in one because Joseph had laid it out and pre-cut as much of the material as was possible in advance. The ground was fairly flat, but we used a water level to make sure the fence was true. There was enough of everything, with just a little to spare.

Joseph's job site mentality carried over here. Planning ahead makes the actual work a game to see if you have built the project in your mind properly. Joseph said, "Always figure 5% extra on material because it seems like there is always something that comes up that you haven't thought of. Planning makes you good, not perfect." That day building the fence, we were good, though I felt like we were perfect.

I was 18. It was Saturday. I had just busted my butt for 12 hours for free. The fence was a job I didn't even have the skill to start on my own, let alone finish, and I felt perfect. Such was the power of Joseph Thunderbull to motivate and teach.

We cleaned the area and stored our tools, then leaned against the fender of the old farm truck. Joseph looked down the fence. It was straight, strong, and true. I felt like we were looking down a hog-high and pig-tight engineer's dream. This was more than a fence—it was a monument to honorable work well done. I looked again and decided it was more even than that—heck, it was art. Joseph's comment as he looked over the project was simple: "It'll do," he said.

"I feel like we should sign it," I said.

He looked at me, grabbed the closest post, and jerked at it hard. It didn't move an eyelash.

Joseph said, "We did. We built it right, and that is the best signature I can think of. We did our best. It reminds me of one of my favorite Bible stories, the widow's mite. Jesus remarks that an old woman giving a single small coin, when all around her are giving much bigger gifts, is giving the best of all. He says hers is the best gift because she holds nothing back. That is why this fence feels so good, Bill—we held nothing back. We gave it our best: we know it, the people we gave it to know it, and the fence knows it.

"You were good help today, Bill; let me thank you properly. Would you join me here tomorrow after worship for a thank-you dinner? How about 4:30 in the afternoon?" Joseph asked.

I considered my nonexistent Sunday schedule briefly, thinking to myself, "I should be up by then," and replied, "Sure."

The next day I arrived right on time and knocked on the side door that led down to Joseph's part of the house. He hollered for me to come in, and I stepped into a different world than I would have ever imagined. It was very neat, which I suppose wasn't so unusual. Many in the trades are fastidious. This was a habit born of an attention to detail in their drive for production and safety. In fact, one measure of an effective job site foreman is control over environmental clutter. I was to learn with experience that control of clutter was a characteristic of every good worker. Dirty job sites speak of safety hazards and lack of organizational coordination—both counterproductive. No, the enigma of this place was not the neatness of it. It was the feel of it. There was a very special spirit about the place.

My first impression as I entered Joseph's apartment was that this was the comfortable living space of a 19th-century English gentleman. I had read of such things in the stories of Sherlock Holmes by Sir Arthur Conan Doyle. I had seen reproductions of such rooms in old movies. Fascinated, I took a breath and came in a couple more steps, enough to see what the room held a bit more clearly. The next thing that came to mind was that I had landed in an unnumbered backroom at the Smithsonian, or a private collection gallery in the Library of Congress. That was how it seemed I suppose—a cross between the private library of a tweed-clad, bespectacled scholar and Indiana Jones's trophy room. In the corner of the room was an overstuffed chair flanked by twin end tables and reading lamps. It was amazing how many books found their homes in this sanctuary. I was, no doubt, in the king-of-reading's throne room.

Hearing me enter, Joseph called again from the kitchen and told me to make myself at home: we would be ready to eat in about five minutes. I looked around again and knew two things instantly—making myself at home here would be no problem, and five minutes wasn't nearly enough time to absorb the wonders of this room.

I was overwhelmed by the peace of the place. There were books everywhere. Joseph had no doubt built many of the shelves: they were beautiful and they were full. Two of the walls were covered floor to ceiling with built-in adjustable shelving. The post in the middle of the room that supported the floor joist above was wrapped on all four sides with a bookcase, and there were even shelves under the end tables and beneath the big oak coffee table. The two shelfless walls were covered with paintings and artifacts. My eyes were drawn to the leather, beadwork, and weapons. Most prominent was a handmade bow in a beautifully fringed and beaded bow case. Below it hung a quiver and arrows. I had never seen such beautiful Native artifacts as these.

There was one more thing so subtle I almost missed it. It was the smell of the place. Not the stale or dank odor of used or old books, but a smell so distinctive it seemed out of place. It was the mixed smell of wood smoke and freshly cut hay, only much sweeter. As impossible as it sounds in a basement apartment, that is exactly what I was smelling.

Joseph called a second time from the kitchen, this time announcing, "Dinner is served."

The kitchen and eating area were small and pleasant. The meal was good, the food was what I would later identify as western ranch-style cooking, and there was plenty of it. Biscuits and sausage gravy, chicken fried steak, corn on the cob, with apple crisp for dessert.

We talked for a while, the kind of small talk that a dinner table and a Sunday afternoon invites. Joseph asked about my father and mother, and we talked briefly about the jobsite.

I asked Joseph if he remembered the day on the

jobsite when Iron Mike said the kids of my generation are doomed by the changes in the world. "He seemed pretty sure. How do you know he is wrong?"

"Mike is a good man, Bill, but he is just a little negative and hopeless about his kids right now. He has two teenage sons who are a little lost, and he is afraid for them. He has done the best he knows how, but they are really struggling. He is frustrated and feels powerless to help—so he just blames the world for their condition. He still believes deep down in his heart they are good boys. What he needed was a little hope. I thought I could spare him some.

"Bill, they are good boys. I believe that life is set up to teach good people—even good people who have made foolish choices—how to find wisdom and joy. I think that will happen if we will be patient and let it. If we honestly keep trying and learning, life will provide the lessons we need. Mike knows that. He would recognize himself in the boys if he would think back to how he grew and learned. He just needed a little reminder."

I asked Joseph about his family. He said he was raised by his father and mother some, but mostly by his paternal grandparents. He and his sister, Sarah, had been raised in the Stillwater country out West. By the time high school came, he went to school early on Monday morning, boarded in town during the week, and returned home on Friday night. The distance to town, combined with the iffy winter weather in the mountains, made living in town during the week the practice of half the kids in his school. Some of the ranches and homes were 40 or more rough miles from paved road. He had enjoyed high school very much and passed the time in the boarding house in town with Sarah, good books, and friends.

His grandmother, Water Singing, was an artist. Most of the paintings and sketches in the room were hers. A mission school teacher had recognized her natural artistic ability and had taken great interest in helping her develop her artistic gifts. After high school his grandmother had attended an art school in Chicago for a semester on a scholarship arranged by her teacher, not a common opportunity for an Indian woman at the turn of the century. She visited many quality museums and galleries in the East just prior to the First World War. Her heart was always in the western mountains, though. Water Singing also knew of healing things in the old way, both for mind and body. She had been taught these things by her mother and her mother's sisters. Her childhood sweetheart, Joseph's grandfather, Kicking Bird, had waited for her to finish her visit in the East, and they married the day she returned to her mountains.

Joseph had gone to school in Montana briefly after high school but decided early on that college was not for him. He loved construction, and for his entire adult life had worked as a carpenter. He believed in the process of apprenticeship and the blessing of working with his hands. He came to understand that we are all apprentices and need mentors in life as in the trades. We learn best by doing.

Without going into detail, Joseph explained that he married a young woman from Boston, whom he described simply as the finest person he had ever known. They lived in Boston while she finished law school, then they moved West and she practiced law in Denver and Billings. They shared five wonderful years together and then life got even better with the birth of their son. Three years after the birth, his wife and son had died in a car wreck, the victims of a drunken driver.

Joseph lived the next two years with his grandparents in the Stillwater. By then, he healed enough to come out of the mountains and work for a while. He found this place and settled into what became his nearly 20-year routine. He would work enough to buy books and save a little for travel and expenses, wander and read, spend some time in the mountains with family, and then return here to work construction again.

I asked why he had not remarried. He replied simply, "Let's go into the living room and sit down." It was clear we were through talking about his wife and son.

As we re-entered the reading king's throne room, I smelled the same smell as before. I described it and asked Joseph what it was. He laughed and said, "That is promise you smell."

He told me the smoky smell was just that—smoke-cured leather. The skins in the room had all been tanned by his sister or grandmother. They tanned the old way—with brains and wood smoke. The campfire smell never completely left hides tanned this way. My host explained that the other smell was sweet grass from the plains of Alberta. It was braided and dried. There was a handle of the braided grass in a basket in the corner. He let me smell a braid about three feet long and as wide as a one-room schoolhouse ruler. The aroma was wonderfully distinctive, and to this day sweetgrass is one of my favorite smells.

"Why do you say it smells like promise?" I asked.

"In the winter, when you must be inside or freeze, the grass smells like the place of a summer fishing camp or the fall hunt. The leather smells like a campfire and the earthy harvest smells of abundance to come. We all need to be reminded that even in the coldest and darkest of times there is always the hope of Father's kindness in giving us a good hunt and the abundance of Mother Earth in providing from the soil. These smells are a reminder of our Mother Earth and our Father Sky and their intention to provide good things for us. This is their intention, even if the winters of our lives try to make us forget. This is the way of all true medicine. It reminds us of our power, who we are, and where we fit.

"It is a wise person who remembers these things. The best medicine should remind us of who we are and that what we know in our hearts has value." He reached into the day pack that was resting against the big chair where he was sitting. I had noticed the day pack at the jobsite— it was his constant companion, and he used it to carry his books and lunch among other things. I had commented on it one day at lunch when he pulled a calculator from it to figure some material quantities. He explained his pack was what the mountain men called a "possible bag," because you keep anything in there you might possibly need. It was never far from his hand.

What he pulled out now surprised me. It was a leather bag I had never seen before. It was buckskin, heavily fringed and well worn. The bag itself was about five inches wide and eight or ten inches long. The fringe hung long and straight down one side of the bag and along the bottom. The flap that served as a closure was held by a button made from the butt of a deer horn. Joseph lifted it reverently and told me this was his medicine bag. It had been a gift from his grandmother and grandfather. He said the fringe was adorned with beads made of glass, metal, and bone, and other items possessing protective powers after the old ways. I noticed in particular a small feather and some carved stones tied into the fringe. He placed it back into the pack without offering me a closer look. Respectfully he spoke of it, "It contains my medicine, the things that are to remind me of who and what I am. It contains healing things prepared for me in the beginning by my grandmother mostly. I have added to its contents over the years, as I came to know what should go inside. It is very strong medicine for me." He paused and sat quietly for a moment.

"Why all the books?" I wondered aloud.

He chuckled quietly before answering, "I have asked myself that very question many times. As far as I can tell, I owe my love of books to five people." Extending one finger, he began the countdown and said, "My grandfather, Kicking Bird, taught me to be an inquisitive person. He taught me that all learning is important. I review the wisdom of Kicking Bird every day. His legacy to me is his wisdom and his love of learning. He was my teacher of the old ways. The knowledge of our people was handed down from fathers, grandfathers, and old uncles to the children. Kicking Bird is my strongest connection to all those things. Perhaps one day we can talk more of Kicking Bird—we will see. I think my grandfather would have liked you . . . and you would have liked him a lot. He taught me to appreciate the magic power of true words.

"My grandmother, Water Singing, taught me how to appreciate beauty. She saw it everywhere. She had the gift of all great artists to see what is there, and what could be there. She taught me to look at the world how it was, how it is, and how it could be. To notice all of it we must use whatever of our senses are needed. Grandmother taught me about the plants we have been given to heal us. She showed me the way to use them and how and when to gather and prepare them. She loved the magic of stories and the motivational power of every kind of beauty. She read books as easily as she read the colors of the morning sky. She loved adventure and mystery whether she found it in a book or a flower.

"Miss Leora Clawson, an old maid teacher in a one-room country elementary school, taught me how to read and gave me the world to explore. Miss Clawson taught me the adventure and possibilities of the written word. She taught me the joy of discovering and learning from what others have seen and learned. She knew the worlds of Marco Polo and the Count of Monte Cristo, and she didn't want me to miss any of them."

He softened as he said, "My wife, Juliet Quince Jones Thunderbull, and Jonathan Thunderbull, our son, taught me how to love and how to be alone. Both of these skills made reading come even more alive for me. These were an unexpected gift from a very hard time. I think these five are mostly responsible for my devotion to books. Feel free to browse through them and take a couple to read if you want. Bring them back when you are done and grab a couple more."

This is how I was introduced to the Thunderbull Memorial Lending Library. When I returned a book we would discuss it, and then he would suggest another. We would debate the merits of what he or I was reading as we worked. Joseph was politically conservative and very patriotic, but sometimes he surprised me as we discussed what we were reading. He said much of what we took for unique current political fervor had been around for centuries in one form or another. He said some of what was now mainstream was not always so. I remember his warning not to judge Ho Chi Minh and Dr. Martin Luther King as too extreme. He said, "Much of what we now call great thought was in its time revolutionary and political, some was mystical, some even popular." He told me that around the 6th century B.C., in a book called *The Odes*, Chai-Fu explored the wickedness of the reigning king by writing, "If you would but change your heart the nations might be fed."

Joseph said, "Sounds a lot like Ho or Dr. King, doesn't it? Who can know what any man thinks unless that man decides to tell? That is why we must learn to speak up, but only when we have thought carefully and have something worth saying." I thought back to the first time I heard Joseph speak—in response to Iron Mike's tirade—and understood better why the others had accepted so fully what he had said.

I was surprised by his varied literary tastes. His books were old and new, classics and obscure, fiction and nonfiction; most were paperback; all were well read. I commented on the obvious variety.

"Are you surprised that a carpenter can read more than blueprints? Maybe you had expected me to stick to more identifiable Indian or western fare? Perhaps you expected a little more Louis L' Amour or the *Time Life: Great Chiefs* series?

"Grandfather told me that all wisdom can be found in the wilderness—and everywhere is wilderness. I'm sure as we become friends, someone will accuse you of being an Indian 'wanna-be' because of your interest in the old wisdom."

He said, "The thing to remember is that most people don't take the time to understand that we are all pretty much alike—or at least generally more alike than different. That is all about ignorance and stereotyping. I don't think wanting to understand Native American wisdom makes you a 'wanna-be' Indian any more than my trying to understand the essentials of rocketry makes me a 'wanna-be' German. Does trying to understanding Lao Tsu make us a 'wanna-be' ancient Chinese sage?"

I didn't think so when he explained it that way. He told me that in most cases it's like Kicking Bird said, "Wisdom is everywhere—if you are looking." The concepts of true wisdom, when discovered, can be applied across the board, across time, and across cultures.

Joseph ended his school session with a touch of humor and one of his favorite cultural tirades. He said, "The overriding truth of this whole discussion is that this or any argument about cultural identity and correctness, no matter how profound it seems, cannot be used to rationalize that ballet or the accordion is socially acceptable in any way, in any time, or in any culture."

Like all of us, Joseph had some biases I could never get my finger on. He almost always mentioned these petty dislikes with lighthearted recognition of his obvious blind spot. Joseph hated ballet and the accordion, but he loved bagpipes and sauerkraut. Go figure.

Joseph recognized the difference between needs and wants. He also understood that each of us has a blind spot or two when it comes to identifying our own.

I remember going to ask Joseph his opinion about a car I wanted to buy. I didn't think he would approve.

The reason I wanted that car, a bright red 1965 Mustang, was not only for transportation but for fun, and, if I am honest, I wanted it for a prestige boost to get girls. I was prepared to hear the worst, but I still asked his opinion. I described the car in all its glory and passionately explained my desire to own it. Then I asked him what he thought I should do. "Joseph," I said, "we have talked about greed and the need to run from it, but I want this car so much it hurts. I'm not sure just what to do."

I knew he believed that personal greed was among the greatest threats to the well-being of all people. This "tribe-before-self" conviction was a cornerstone of his concept of personal integrity. What I had not counted on was that Joseph also knew the importance and power of positive rewards in our lives, and he loved me.

His answer about the car was classic Thunderbull: "I can tell you for sure what I know: You should always seek that which is pure. This is wisdom. There are very few things in the world that are pure. At this moment, in truth, I can think of only three: Reading *To Kill a Mockingbird* for the first time, the feeling you get when you wake early to go fishing, and a red 1965 Ford Mustang."

He was a great teacher and a very insightful friend. I always loved that car.

Our first Sunday visit blends in my memory with the many that followed. Some of the warmest and funniest days I ever spent were in the basement library at Joseph's city house.

Chapter Three

The Stillwater

Where you find good people,
stay at that place and be among them.

✣

The Stillwater Buckskin

I really saw Joseph as a person for the first time when we went to the mountains to fish. Thinking back, there were actually several firsts on that trip: I met Sarah and the boys; I met Joseph's friend and mentor, Gordon Paints His Horses; and I was introduced to the sacred mountains of Joseph's youth. It started one day on the job when I mentioned that my dad and I had fly fished as I was growing up, and I longed to fish the trout streams of the Rockies.

Joseph surprised me by saying that he loved to fly fish. He said the drainages around the Sweetwater were full of small trout streams—many with beaver ponds. These streams didn't get much pressure from fishermen, other than the locals who knew how to access them. I was to be off to school that fall, so we hatched a plan right then to make a fly fishing trip to the mountains in late summer before I left for my first year at the university.

My father had taught me to fly fish. It was one of the few things we did together. I loved the sport—it was simple and more like hunting than the bait fishing many of my friends did. However, if I am truly honest with myself, I love to fly fish for trout mostly because I love where trout live, the western mountains most of all. I love small mountain streams for their intimacy. I am convinced that the clean purity of a high mountain stream is one of God's greatest gifts to man. When I learned of Joseph's affection for fly fishing, it drew us closer and provided endless hours of fishing conversation and speculation. It was the chance to fly fish in the small creeks of Joseph's beloved Stillwater that first took me to his home.

That trip to the mountains with Joseph was the first time I realized the importance and impact of self-disclosure on relationships. This trip taught me that taking the time to talk can bring people closer faster than almost anything. I discovered that communication is more than just taking turns talking. I was amazed as we talked at what Joseph and I had in common and what we didn't. For two days as we drove we listened to the radio and talked about everything that came to mind—from God to our favorite kinds of pie, from the mating habits of caddis flies to Yoko Ono's destruction of the Beatles. On the jobsite, Joseph had accepted me as a partner. On that trip I accepted the fact we had become friends.

Joseph's place in the Stillwater was a wing of the log house he shared with his sister, Sarah, and her sons. This was to be our base of operations for the week. We drove into Sarah's place just before dark and were greeted by several farmyard dogs and the smell of wood smoke. We got out of the car and did the time-honored four-straight-hours-without-standing stretch and twist. The dogs sniffed us and served as our escorts to the house.

We stepped onto the front porch and walked to the kitchen door. By this time Joseph had told me a lot about Sarah and her boys. The only comment I ever heard about her husband was that he was "long gone." However, what I had pictured in my mind as Joseph's sister was far from the woman who greeted us at the door.

She was what my grandmother would have called "as small as a minute," but that would have been about 30 seconds too long. She was about 5'1" and weighed at most one hundred pounds. She was a very pretty, very petite woman with long black braids flecked with gray. Her eyes were bright, intense, and pale green. Joseph told me God had made up for her lack of physical size by giving her the soul of a mountain. Looking into those eyes I knew he had not exaggerated. She embraced her brother, then looked at me and said, "You must be the white boy." I admitted I was. "Welcome to the Stillwater, young man. Please come in and eat."

Two things struck me as I entered the house. The first was the hot, dry smell of the wood cook stove. The second was the feeling that it was home—not only was it my home, but home to anybody who was invited in. Joseph's part of the house was in the back. We dropped our bags there and washed up. His living quarters had two separate bedrooms, a reading room, and a bathroom. The reading room was not unlike the reading room in the city house.

As I washed up for dinner, I noticed several things that reminded me of the bathroom at my grandparents' farm: a huge white porcelain tub with legs—the handles on the sink and tub were the old porcelain "X" type. There was a straight razor, a brush and mug, and a cake of Old Spice shaving soap. The small, four-pane window was high on the wall above the tub and had hinges on the bottom. It was open about 20 degrees and was held at each top corner by chains attached to the window frame. The comfortable familiarity of the place was tied together by the squeak of my feet on the ancient flowered linoleum. I finished washing up and walked back through the reading room to the warmth of Sarah's kitchen and one of the best dinners of my life. Sarah wore a long-sleeved western cut, crisp white cotton shirt, Levi's, and cowboy boots. She moved like Joseph, wasting no time or motion. She was pleased to have company, and it was clear she loved her brother.

I noticed two more things about her that reminded me of Joseph. First, as she worked, she sang peacefully in just audible but not identifiable tones. Second, on her right hip, attached to her belt, she wore a small fringed medicine bag very much like the one Joseph had shown me, only this one was white doeskin as opposed to the buckskin color of Joseph's bag. The bag was adorned with beads, carved stones, and elk ivory. It made very soft bell sounds as she moved. That was ever the sound of Sarah.

I fell asleep that night, and every other night I spent in Sarah and Joseph's house over the years, to the peculiar breathing sound made by the small fuel oil stove in Joseph's part of the house. As the stove drew air from the outside to feed the low flame, it sounded like a gentle wind in far-away trees. There was a small window in the front of the stove so you could see when it was lit. It provided just enough dancing light to give the impression of a dying fire.

Sarah and the boys were already gone when we got up. She worked at the head start school three days a week and started the 40-mile drive early. The creek we fished that morning was small but very productive, and we talked little as we fished upstream in leap frog fashion from hole to hole. Joseph would stop occasionally to show me something that he thought I might find interesting—how the almost heart-shaped hoof marks of a doe coming to drink were distinctive from those of a buck; where elk had bedded in the grassy seep of a small spring to keep cool in the summer heat. He mentioned mountain plants and birds, spearmint on the creek bank, Brigham tea, Sego Lilly, watercress. I saw my first king fisher, and we sat and watched an osprey hunt fish—just as we were doing.

Joseph told me we were going to see Gordon Paints His Horses that night. Gordon was the last of his grandfather's friends who was still living. Joseph described him as a fine old gentleman, a good horseman, and a real Indian. That afternoon as we prepared to go to Gordon's, Joseph unpacked a gallon jar. He had put the jar on dry ice in a Coleman cooler and duct taped it shut before we left home. When I asked what was in the jar, Joseph smiled and held it up, "A gallon of fresh-shucked oysters. You can't get them here," he said, "and the old man loves them. They were his favorite thing about World War I. Gordon once told me the two best things that he got out of World War I was a love of oysters and his first green wool army blanket."

As we packed the truck, Joseph told me we'd be staying overnight at Gordon's house. It was about a 60-mile drive, and there were some nearby creeks we would fish on the following day. As we rode, Joseph told me Gordon was a bit of a local legend. His grandfather had been a cavalry scout, his father an Indian policeman, and Gordon had been a doughboy in WWI. He lived on a piece of property near where his grandfather had been born. Some Chinese miners had established a claim on the land in the late 1800s. After they had worked the claim out, Joseph's father had purchased the land. It had been in their family ever since. It was bordered on three sides by federal forest. It was quiet and very remote.

We crossed two large cattle ranches on a well-used gravel road after leaving the highway before we finally got to the gate at Gordon's place. By this time I was familiar with the routine of what to do when we came to a closed barbed wire gate. I would jump from the truck, run to the gate, remove the top barbed wire loop from the gate post, lift the post from the bottom loop, and pull the gate wide open. After Joseph had driven the truck through, I would replace the gate by standing the post in the bottom loop and pushing the top of the post until I could pull the top barbed wire loop over it. We had gone through six or seven such gates before we got to the one that led into Gordon's yard.

The main house was a sturdily built log structure. There were several outbuildings and a couple of corrals, one of which was a round horse-breaking pen about 40 feet across and 12 or 14 feet high. Joseph told me that Gordon, after returning from World War I, had spent most of his life as a ranch hand, breaking and trading horses on the side. He had lived here with his wife, two sons, and two daughters. His wife had passed away about 20 years before. One of his daughters lived down in town. The other daughter and two boys had moved to Denver to work. All the kids and their families visited home occasionally to spend time with the old man.

Among the outbuildings was a chicken coop and what turned out to be a long line of rabbit hutches. They were accompanied by a small barn and smaller equipment shed. The water for the house came from a year-round spring up the mountain 200 yards. A pipe tapped it below ground and filled a concrete-lined stone cistern that kept the house constantly supplied with good, sweet, mountain spring water. The spring flowed into the small creek that ran between the barn and sheds, then down toward the road we had traveled and eventually to the river. It was a good stream of water. Gordon's father had been one of the first in the area to have an indoor bathroom and water supplied right to the kitchen sink.

It was clear the ranch had electricity. The yard light illuminated the place pretty well. A tall slender man who looked to be in his 60s (Joseph told me later he was in his mid-90s) walked out of the screen door, across the front porch, and out to the truck. He wore a western-cut shirt, a Montana-creased Stetson, cowboy boots, and a wide belt with a rodeo buckle that attested to some past achievement. A pair of work gloves hung comfortably out his back pocket. Had it not been for the Roman nose and dark skin, he could have been any hand on any ranch in the West, but this man was obviously one of The People.

He helped us unload the truck and invited us in to a meal of baking powder biscuits and sausage gravy. He augmented this at the last minute by several helpings of raw oysters, oysters poached in cream, and oysters drenched in milk, rolled in Corn Flakes, and then pan fried. Everything was delicious. Later, after we helped Gordon clean up and wash the dishes, we sat quietly by the old stone hearth. When an appropriately respectful length of quiet time had passed, Joseph politely inquired about the old man's family, and then about his personal health. Gordon said he was well, and that the kids and grandkids were great. He asked about Sarah and the boys. Sarah's oldest son, Johnson, was a real favorite of his and often stayed with him during the summer and other school breaks. He said Johnson had the gift with horses, though he didn't know it yet. The boy would be a good hand. Gordon then turned to me and asked how my family was, where they were, who they were, and why I had chosen to come fishing in these mountains with Joseph Thunderbull. I explained my love for fly fishing. He said he had never been, but would probably ride out tomorrow and watch us if we were close by. He loved fish, brook trout especially, and asked if we would keep him a couple tomorrow.

As we sat, he told us stories from his youth, from just last summer, and from all points between. Gordon was a gifted storyteller, a master of understatement and charm. He talked briefly to Joseph about how much he missed his wife, and Joseph's grandparents, Water Singing and Kicking Bird. He turned to me and explained that Kicking Bird was the last of the medicine men from his youth to die. He said Kicking Bird had passed on his shaman's wisdom and skills to the man I had come to call my friend, Joseph Thunderbull. This came as a surprise to me, and I wanted to know more, but this was Gordon's time and Joseph didn't seem to even acknowledge the comment.

The training Gordon received from his own father was based on one of the warrior societies. His uncle had taught him to catch, raise, and train horses. The same uncle taught him to trade horses. From this uncle he had learned the trick of painting horses. From this unusual skill came his family name.

The old man told me that Joseph had been trained by his grandfather and was now called on occasionally to sing the sacred songs, as Kicking Bird had been before his death. Joseph again made no comment, so we moved on to other subjects. We talked of weather, game, and horses. Gordon recalled the days of his youth and asked if my mother canned peaches. He said he thought in the world to come, most main dishes would be some kind of oysters, and as accompaniment, we would always have peaches canned by our own mothers. The peaches would no doubt be cold and served with lots of fresh cream.

Joseph and I slept that night in what I had originally thought was a chicken coop. Half of it was—the other half was a bunkhouse. A fire had been laid in the stove in the corner: the room was already warm when we entered. The night passed peacefully.

I was awakened before dawn by the sound of Joseph and the old man chatting as Joseph chopped wood. I went out and joined them. Joseph and I used an old two-man saw to buck the logs into 24-inch sections, and as we split Gordon stacked it. It was obvious to me that one of the reasons we had come was to help put up the old man's winter wood, which we did, breaking only for breakfast until about four in the afternoon. It was also clear to me that the old man had not asked Joseph to do this task, but had expected he would. Logs had been dragged up in a pile. The wood shed was almost empty, and the obvious transition from log pile to the security of split winter firewood was just waiting for Joseph's visit. It was a pleasant day, passed in reminiscent conversation. Every time a subject even remotely related to the medicine tradition came up, Joseph seemed to change the subject. I thought it was because of some kind of secret; I would find out later that Joseph simply wanted to make sure I was genuinely interested. He was a humble man, not predisposed to personal horn tooting. He understood that with knowledge comes responsibility, and I think he wanted to make sure that I was willing to pay the price for receiving the knowledge that he had to share with me.

Joseph understood that with every opportunity comes a responsibility. Such trusts are the price we pay for understanding. Life gives us all choices, and Joseph was fond of reminding me life was ten percent what happened and ninety percent what you did with it.

That afternoon, after a quick lunch of sandwiches made of thick-sliced cheese and bologna, followed by a glass of cold mountain water and a dish of home-canned peaches with cream, the wood pile was finished. We grabbed our fly rods and walked about a half mile to a lively stream full of brook trout. The fishing was wonderful—challenging enough to be stimulating, active enough to be rewarding.

We hadn't been at it long when Gordon joined us to watch the fun. He rode a beautiful Appaloosa gelding, a tall horse with an intelligent face. He was the typical dark-bodied horse with a white rump, beautifully spotted; on his right front shoulder, as clear as could be, was a Star of David the size of a dinner plate. I was amazed to see the marking and asked Gordon if it was painted on. Gordon chuckled and said, "No, the hair there grows white."

Horse painting was a trick he'd learned from his uncle. It wasn't really painting at all, but a process to turn dark hair into white in any pattern or shape. His uncle had been taught how by an old Apache horse trader many, many years before. It was useful in two ways, he told me: in the old days when you stole someone's young horse, you could change its appearance and the hair would always be white in the place where you made the change. The other reason was that the white man simply loved the look of the beautiful paint horses of the Plains Indians. So, Gordon's father and grandfather had taken plain dark horses and made them into paints. They finally had to quit selling the altered horses locally because all of them had nothing but plain dark-colored offspring. Everyone felt cheated and knew it was some kind of trick.

Gordon admitted it was a trick, but a good trick. He no longer traded horses, but still marked all his stock on the right front shoulder just to irritate Mr. Larson at the local animal auction. Larson had offered many times to pay Gordon if he would show him the secret of "painting" horses. Gordon chuckled and said he never would because Larson was not a man he liked much. I asked him how he did it and he told me it had to do with blowing hot steam through a freshly baked potato. He didn't say much beyond that and I've always wondered if he was kidding about how it was done, though Joseph said he was not. We all enjoyed the obvious joke on old Mr. Larson. I noticed the following day that every horse on the place, and I saw about 20, had an unusual patch of white hair on his right front shoulder. In one case, it was the letter "G", about 12 inches high. The old cowboy did enjoy his fun.

On our second morning Gordon started us off with a breakfast of scrambled eggs and oysters, and for lunch I was satisfied with a Hostess pie, and some bologna, cheese, and crackers. I noticed that Gordon fried up some more oysters. That night we had brook trout. Gordon decided he'd add some oysters; it was obvious that the gallon jar wouldn't last long.

Around the stove that evening, we continued our conversation from the night before. Gordon told us of leaving home for World War I—a trip to France, although he never saw action and returned home immediately after the war. He'd worked as a cowboy on most of the local ranches and was well respected as a hand. Joseph knew most of the local ranchers, both white and Indian, as did Gordon. Joseph had gone to school with many of their kids. It was a pleasant and happy place to grow up.

We talked later that night about hunting. Gordon loved to hunt and still spent as much time as possible in the mountains. He asked me if I had ever been hunting. When I said I hadn't, he told me that the next fall I was welcome to come back and hunt elk with Joseph from his place. We could stay at Sarah's or we were welcome to stay with him. There were two big ranches next door where he and Joseph often hunted. He had decided not to hunt any more, but said he would love some meat if we got any. It was there that the plans were hatched for my elk hunt the next fall, around the wood stove in the cabin of Gordon Paints His Horses, high in the western mountains.

The following morning we left Gordon's place, and for the next several days made the rounds of several ranches, both Indian and white, saying hello and checking in on those people for whom Joseph had special affection. I noticed whenever we stopped, Joseph had a small gift to give. When we stopped at the house of an older friend or relative, we took the time to do some small chore—fix a latch, split or haul some wood, or pull some wire to close a hole in a pasture fence. Every time we stopped I remembered Joseph's favorite Bible story—the widow's mite. He often gave only small things, but it was what he had. When it came to those he loved, he held nothing back.

For Joseph every day was a chance to learn something new. He was an observer. We stopped to see a favorite aunt. She was making a basket. Joseph watched her prepare the willows for weaving by soaking them in water. He told me she used a local herb in the water to help the willow become more flexible. He used the trick later to help form the back of a rocking chair for his house. I Q is not just smarts, said Joseph, it is mostly the ability and flexibility to generalize the knowledge gained in one place to help in another.

Slowly I was learning the way of Joseph Thunderbull. What I didn't realize until much later, I was learning the way of any real man among his people. All was not work and visiting. We did a lot of fishing and eventually prepared to say good-bye to Sarah and be on our way. We had spent a final night in her home, ate a good dinner, and were soundly thrashed in a game of Scrabble. I learned from Sarah that much of Joseph's income over the years was sent to her and the boys, old Gordon, and two or three other families in the mountains. The more I learned about Joseph Thunderbull, the more I could see why he was at peace and happy with himself. At the end of the week, we returned home. The ride back to the city was as pleasant, entertaining, and informative as the ride to the mountains had been. We got home on Sunday, had a good night's sleep, and were back on the job site Monday morning.

Shortly after our return from the Stillwater, I was off to school. I enjoyed college and dropped the occasional note to Joseph. School introduced me to more great thinkers, great teachers, and great people. I met my wife that first year. We dated throughout our four years of studies and married after graduation. We made occasional trips to the mountains, and Rebecca and I learned to love the people there. She was particularly fond of Sarah and wrote her often, exchanging family news. I made a few friends and enjoyed the process of falling in love with Rebecca.

Joseph loved her too. She called him on occasion, and when we visited home we always joined him for Sunday dinner. After dinner we would sit in his reading room and discuss what one or the other of us was reading. From time to time we would sit and solve the problems of the world together. I was amazed at how many of the books that I had read from Joseph's "library" or discussed with him were required or referred to throughout my college experience. I was discovering that great minds and hearts from every time and culture share the same journey. Life is designed to test us all.

I had wonderful professors for the most part. Joseph taught me to not let my formal schooling interfere with my education. On those occasions when my professors were not what they had once been or what they could have been, I tried to learn how not to be. I learned how to love the message in spite of, not because of, the messenger. I came to see the truth of what Joseph had taught me about the real masters of any subject. Masters are those for whom what they do still matters. They are the teachers of life who find a way to contribute, no matter what the setting. They are the professors who teach because they have to—if they didn't they would explode. So, when I was fortunate enough to encounter one of these I tried to get all he or she had to offer. When I encountered someone who had lost his or her teaching medicine, for whom the fire had become mere embers, I tried to love the subject and imagine the light and warmth of past fires. I knew during that first year that people were the real meaningful fabric of all I did. I was blessed to be surrounded by great ones.

After my first year of college, I spent another summer working beside Joseph. That fall I took him up on his invitation to hunt elk. It was to be a very significant point in my life—my first experience with the wilderness and the bounty and awesome power of it. It was to teach me gratitude and respect.

Chapter Four

The First Hunt

Observe everything,
and by observing
be taught.

The Stillwater Buckskin

I started to worry as we left the truck the first morning before dawn.

"What happens if we get separated?" I asked Joseph.

"Before the sun goes down, we'll meet at the place we started from. That rule will always be the same whether we are hunting, fishing, or at the shopping center. Before the sun goes down, we will always return to the place we started that day. That is why we must always look carefully at the starting point. If we are to find our way back, we must know where we want to end up. Every place has its own way of looking and feeling. As you walk, take time to look back. Things always look different going the other direction. Take your bearings by picking landmarks that are easy to identify. This rockslide is big and you would think it would make a good thing to remember, but look around. There are three other such rock slides we can see from here. They look smaller only because they are farther away. They are the same color and the same kind of rock. Even though this slide looks like the important thing to remember here, it is not. The big thing is not always the thing that will guide you home."

"So what do we look for?" I asked.

"Well," Joseph said, in his most stoic, here-comes-a-lesson way, "The first thing I look for before going into an unknown place is a good map and a great compass. Take the time to study where you are going before you get there. That's half the fun anyway. Where do you want to go? What is your purpose? What do you want to see? Where is the access? How safe is it? Is it worth the effort? If you kill an animal, are you willing to pack it out? Do you have the time and the strength? Do you have a way to get enough food and shelter if you are hurt? If you are alone, have you told anybody where you are going?"

He continued, "After all is said, though, people get lost even with a compass and a map. You could get hurt or have a bout of food poisoning. You could have a fall and be disoriented. You could drop your pack or lose it in a snow slide. In the wilderness anything could happen. That is why we live—to find out how we will respond to life's tests. The final rule is this: if you are lost, take time to assess your resources. Inventory your belongings, take your bearings and remember to pay attention, sit quietly and be thankful for your awareness and wellness. When that has been done, look downhill and find a way to the nearest water. Follow the line of the ridge you are on until you find a stream. In the mountains that will be easy. Then follow the course of the water from the game trail that will always be just in or below the tree line. Don't go right to the water except to drink—it will wind and the lowest ground will likely be brushy and swampy. Follow the water until it runs into a bigger stream. Eventually you will be found." Then with a glint in his eye he said, "One hint—if you get to New Orleans, you have gone too far. Find a pay phone and call."

Exasperated, I said, "Hold on! I just asked if we are separated what should I do. All of a sudden I am wondering if I should ever go anywhere in the wilderness again."

Joseph smiled and said we could continue the lecture on wilderness survival later at the cabin. "For now," he said, "I will be finished. Remember two things for today though—first, if you want to hunt elk you have to go where they live. Second, if I were you, I would not get separated from the guy with the map and the compass until you have your own and are a whole lot smarter and more experienced."

We started then on what would be one of the longest and best days of my life. I was in great shape for a kid from sea level, but we weren't at sea level. The high mountain air was thin and with any exertion at all I had to work for every breath. Joseph moved out at a ground-eating pace just below my I-can't-breathe threshold. He knew the country, and he knew he didn't want to have to carry me out of it.

We walked for an hour or so. Joseph stopped at a small outcrop of rock on the spine of a ridge and got out his field glasses. He never ceased to amaze me. The optics he had in his pack cost more than my car. They were Swiss made, and I had only seen them in catalogues.

"Nice binoculars," I said.

He said nothing and continued to glass the creek bottoms several hundred feet below and a mile away. Eventually, I caught on, so I got out my binoculars and started glassing the small valley as well.

I had been deer hunting several times but had never seen an elk in the wild—only in movies and on TV. I was excited and ready to move on after a quick look around the little watershed. According to my eyes, there was not a bit of life in the area. Joseph's wise counsel kept running through my head, "If you want to hunt elk you have to go where they live." Obviously we were not there yet, but Joseph just sat and looked. I got out my canteen and took a drink, ate a candy bar, and began again to sweep the small valley with my field glasses. I finished my search, but Joseph still just sat and looked.

I waited for what seemed like another ten minutes or so, and when I couldn't stand the silence any longer I asked Joseph what he was doing.

He responded without taking his eyes from the glasses, "I'm hunting elk."

Knowing Joseph as I did, I knew he had said all he intended to. So I picked up my glasses and started another sweep.

"What are you looking for?" he asked.

"Duh . . . elk," I said.

He must have recognized that I was ready now to learn. Patiently he explained to me that they would be lying down by this time of day or grazing slowly in the trees or low brush. They would have come to the creek for water that morning and would now be moving toward their beds. For most of the day they would stay bedded down. The biggest bulls would be the most wary—they would be in the thickest timber and would be down by now. The rut was just starting, and the bulls had already moved down closer to the cows and started bunching them up to form a harem for the breeding that was to come.

"What are you looking for?" I asked. Only a slightly different question than I had asked before but one he apparently approved of.

"Duh . . ." he said. "Elk. I can see only six for now, all cows, but I know I am missing a lot. There is at least one big bull here and probably two. The wind is swirling around, so I don't want to go any lower on the hill side until it favors us. I'd just as soon sit here and watch as chase this bunch over the hill with our stink. They don't know we are here and I intend to keep it that way until we kill one."

He took a minute and pointed out the elk he could see feeding. They were beautiful. No wonder I had missed them though. They were moving hardly at all as they grazed. In the timber and brush only the occasional piece of hide could be seen. Once you had them spotted, however, you could stay on them and get a good glimpse from time to time as they moved.

Joseph then showed me the wallow where they had rolled in the mud to protect against the flies and other insects. He pointed out a young sapling that a bull had sparred with to get the velvet off his antlers and take out some aggression.

I watched again for a long time and asked the Indian how he knew there was a big bull and maybe two in such a little valley.

"Two reasons. First, I'm an Indian and I know these things. Second, the truth is I saw him feeding over there by that big tree night before last." We sat right there just inside the shade line most of the day. We had our lunch and talked. Joseph told me more about the habits of the elk. He taught me that when glassing for an animal that is bedded down, it's often best to look at the base of a rim rock, cliff, or slide where they can't be seen from above and yet can see all of the approaches to their hiding place. Without doubt, they have a good sense of hearing and sight. But more than anything else, they depend on their sense of smell.

Elk always keep the wind in their faces—though not always directly into it, sometimes quartering across it to survey what potential for danger is ahead. They generally walk along ridge lines, and they bed on side hills where it is almost impossible to sneak up on them without being seen. Elk will walk up to five miles for a drink of water, often drinking in a creek and crossing it, rarely going back in the same way they've come. They tend to follow general travel patterns, making big figure eights or circles, depending upon the wind, to go from one bedding or drinking spot to another.

Mule deer, on the other hand, don't like to walk more than about two miles for a drink. Mule deer bucks generally bed down in one of three or four favorite beds every day. They're nocturnal, so big mule deer are the hardest animals in the world to hunt and kill within the seasons and hunting times allotted. If we could hunt them during the rut, we could kill them all.

"Like a lot of people I know," Joseph said, "all bets are off during the rut. They get foolish and ignore the behaviors that have protected them throughout the rest of the year. They don't think—they just sniff and paw and get so focused on each other they give the predator the edge."

As the sun began to cast late afternoon shadows, the dozing and grazing animals began to move toward the water. A bull far below and to our left bugled to announce his eminent arrival. Another whistled from what sounded like miles away. As the closer bull kept moving toward the waterhole, he paused every few steps to call out challenges and advertise his presence to any cows or prospective rivals.

When the bull finally stepped into the small meadow I was speechless. I saw what I was sure was astonishment on Joseph's face. He turned to me and said, "This is not the bull I saw the other night. This is his dad. He is very big, six points on each side of his rack. His horns are massive." Joseph looked again, and confirmed his original assessment. "He is a six by six at least or even six by seven."

I asked if we were going to try and move into position for a shot.

Without taking his eyes from the huge trophy, he said, "No. The light will be gone in less than an hour and we must not risk our chance at him by rushing into this. Some things in life can be done routinely—hunting and killing this bull will not be one of those."

"Before we attempt to harvest this bull, we must prepare ourselves," Joseph said.

As we hiked back to the truck, Joseph began to sing softly. He had started his hunting prayer. The question he was asking with his song was how to kill the big bull and what the price would be. As we drove home Joseph said he would explain in the morning what we would have to do to have a chance at this bull. We returned to Gordon's house and slept. The rules of preparation greeted me before dawn as Joseph awakened me the next morning.

"There will be no drinking of anything but water," he told me. "The only spice we will use in our cooking is salt. We will prepare for a two-day hunt, one to get our shot, and a day to pack it out. Today we will build a sweat lodge and get the smell of the world off us. After we have sweat, we will wash in the creek, no soap, and dry ourselves with clean sand."

"I have washed our hunting clothes and put them in a sealed bag after air drying them and sprinkling them with cow elk urine. We will dress in the open air and rub our hands, arms, and hair with sage brush and crushed pine needles. We must contemplate how we will repay the forest for taking the bull. For everything we take or use, there is a price. That price must always be considered in advance. If it is too high, don't take or use the thing."

Because I had seen the bull, I was okay with the effort of preparation—that is, all except the elk urine part, but I was sure Joseph was kidding about that. He was not.

We talked of the price we were willing to pay for the bull as we sat in the sweat lodge we constructed. We must leave the gut pile close to the kill. This will bless the other animals of the valley. We could have the heart, stomach, and liver, but must leave everything else for the forest. We would give meat to Gordon and others who could no longer hunt, or who did not know how. This meat must include some of the choicest cuts; Joseph said some of the best meat should also come to our table. If we took all the best, that would be unkind; if we took none of the best, that would not show the proper respect for our family or for the elk bull. We must haul all the meat, hide, and horns out: the meat first and then the cape and antlers. All must be used for a good purpose. The last thing was to leave some salt where the bull fell. This was a gift to remember that place.

When we got back we must remember to teach others if we had learned new things about hunting. Not giving this information would be selfish if someone needed to feed his children. We spent the rest of the day in and around the sweat lodge on the hill behind Gordon's place, singing and preparing for the hunt.

The alarm was set for 2:30 A.M. I turned it off at 2:20. I knew I had slept, but I wasn't sure how much. What I was sure of was that I had looked at the red numbers of the clock a hundred times since going to bed. I dressed and walked to the yard—Joseph was there, truck running. We rode quietly, with only the occasional soft note of a prayer song Joseph sang under his breath accompanying the stillness of the morning. After we parked the truck at the trail head, we walked to the ridge where we had glassed the elk.

"Do as we planned," said Joseph. "Follow the next ridge down and cross below the water hole. Put your back against the rock chimney, and when the bull passes you to go for water, shoot him. The breeze is slight and in your favor. Shortly after he passes, he will wind you, so don't hesitate. We have done what we can do. If he does offer himself, take the shot. If he is hit and goes down, or runs off, wait for me. I will be watching and listening from here. Don't push him. Let him lay down to die. Stay put and rest. I will come then and we will track him."

With the help of a pen light I made my way to the rock chimney across the small valley. I sat and tried to slow my breathing. Slowly my heart seemed to return to its normal rhythm. I hadn't been sitting long when I heard the far-off whistle of a bull elk. It was just starting to get light. The bull I heard was at least a mile down the valley and moving away. After all we had done, had we miscalculated? Joseph was a good hunter, we had prepared well, but perhaps it was not meant to be.

Just then the big bull we were after screamed his warning reply to the challenge from down the valley. I was so startled by the closeness of the bull and the intensity of his challenge, I froze. There, not 30 yards away and just silhouetted in the first moments of dawn, was the monarch bull. How I had missed the sound of his coming I didn't know. I could hear his breathing, shaking, and grunting as his scream ended and he pawed the earth.

I raised my rifle, placed the cross hairs of the scope just behind his huge front shoulder, gently exhaled, and squeezed the trigger . . . nothing. Then I remembered the safety, and clicked it off with my right thumb. The noise of the safety seemed very loud in the still morning. The bull heard the click. His head came around sharply, but instead of running away, he simply turned his body slightly and bugled his challenge again, even more fiercely and vehemently than before. I squeezed again: this time the rifle jumped in my hands and the bull's knees buckled. He went down and did not move. I sat and waited quietly for Joseph, not knowing whether to cheer or cry. I was shaking and my heart was pounding, but somehow I managed to stay in my stony seat.

Joseph came quickly. We walked to the bull and made sure he was dead. I stood quietly. I couldn't believe the size of the animal. Joseph congratulated me, then sat briefly before the great bull and thanked him. As he prepared to field dress him Joseph told the elk of the families he would give life to and the songs that would be sung of his sustaining gift to those families. We dressed the animal and packed him out over the next several hours. Joseph was singing constantly as we worked. I assumed they were songs of gratitude, so I asked him, "What are you singing, Joseph? Songs of thanks?"

"Yes," he said. "And it is also wise to be loud enough to make sure the other predators know we are still on the kill. I figure if any medicine will keep the bears away it will be my singing." Having heard Joseph's singing many times, I think he was right. The last thing we did was give final thanks and leave a gift of salt on the ground where the bull had fallen.

We took the trophy back to Gordon's place, where we cut, ground, and wrapped the meat. We ate and sang as we worked. Later we delivered it, told the story, and showed the horns. The thanks of all the people who got meat was gratifying. I took the horns and a few choice steaks and roasts. The cape I gave to Sarah. Joseph accepted excellent cuts for grilling, some lesser quality meat for making jerky, and my thanks. I felt for those few days like a man full grown. I was not, as my next hunt would prove.

Chapter Five

Getting Lost

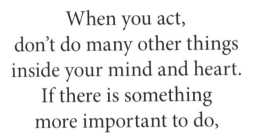

When you act,
don't do many other things
inside your mind and heart.
If there is something
more important to do,
stop and do that thing.

🔹

The Stillwater Buckskin

That year at school was the end of my general education classes. I would begin my climb up the business ladder the next fall as I focused on my major—business, or as my fellow students called it, money 101.

I joined Joseph for another hunt at Gordon's place the fall after I had killed the big bull.

The summer had passed quickly with Joseph and I working together as usual. We went to the mountains to fish twice that summer. Once we took Rebecca with us. She stayed with Sarah while we roamed the valleys and enjoyed the fishing. Johnson, Sarah's oldest son, was staying with Gordon that summer so there was room to spare at the house. We talked many times of the old ways. Sarah showed Rebecca some of the best plants for tea or healing. Joseph told us about how the world began, and both he and Sarah shared some of the fables of their childhood.

Several times during our visits Joseph was called on to sing for sick people. I accompanied him twice on such occasions. He told me these traditional prayers and the herbal healing that accompanied them were taught to him by his grandparents. We hunted arrowheads and Joseph showed me how to identify ancient buffalo kill sites and hunting places. It was a summer to be remembered.

I learned on the job site as well. Joseph was a fine carpenter and continued my training in that field. He continually helped and directed me. It seemed like there was something new every day. Joseph said it didn't matter what the trade, when you don't learn every day you have cheated yourself.

That fall Joseph and I went to the Stillwater to hunt for the second time. The first day of elk season I felt capable of hunting the morning alone to get the lay of the land. With luck, I could spot an animal to kill that afternoon when Joseph joined me. He was to spend the morning with Gordon visiting old friends, so I decided to hunt a few hours alone to spot game. I left the truck just before dawn.

I don't know exactly when I realized I was lost. All at once I looked around and nothing looked or felt familiar. Worse yet, it dawned on me that I had been completely unaware of my surroundings for some time.

I had acted without thinking. I had moved without bearings. As I fought to control the panic rising in my chest, the quiet words of Joseph spoken more than a year before came into my mind, or more correctly, the words of Abraham Lincoln quoted by Joseph, "The first thing a man should do when he finds himself in a hole is stop digging."

Lincoln knew what was up. Joseph had said, "Observe, plan, and act . . . before you let your emotions lead you to the nearest lemming-crowded jumping point. Clean your heart and head, and take charge of your direction."

The lesson had its desired effect. I stopped digging, so to speak—then I sat down, said a brief mind-clearing prayer, and decided on my next step.

I sat quietly for a moment and listed my mistakes. I had left the belt pouch containing my compass and maps in the truck. When I first realized my mistake, it was only a half hour before light, and that's about how long it would have taken to go back and get it. Why should I go back? It was only a morning hunt and I was familiar with the country. I had been here before, or just north of here, when I killed the big bull. The weather was good, and I had to go back and meet Joseph at the truck for the evening hunt anyway. I could get the pouch then. If I went back now, I would miss my chance at seeing a moving bull going to his bed at daybreak. If I didn't get a shot I would go back to the truck. I would be there in time to strap the pouch to my belt before Joseph came and noticed I had forgotten it—and he would notice.

The small valley was on my left as the trail crested the fourth ridge, just as Joseph had said it would be. I tested the wind and left the trail carefully to keep the spine of the ridge at my back and the wind in my face. I figured I should be downwind of the waterhole and 50 or so yards up the hillside from the valley floor when the dawn came. That is exactly where I was.

I first heard the bulls as I slipped into the little Aspen grove that would hide me when light came. My timing seemed perfect. The quakies were small this high up and had already turned the bright yellow gold of fall. It had been a moist fall so the ground cover made little noise as I slipped into the trees. I sat and waited for dawn. Soon my patience was rewarded by an incredible event. I heard two bulls—one on my left by the sound of it and one on my right—both about 500 yards out. They were talking to each other, and it was clear they were arranging a brief meeting and discussion at the waterhole.

I was captivated—the whistle of a bull elk in rut is one of the most primal sounds in nature. Sort of like the emotion of a high school football locker room before the big game—times ten. The bull to my right came crashing down the hill toward the arranged meeting. As he came he voiced his challenge, and I decided to translate in my head: "I'm the real deal, the only stud this mountain can hold, so get your butt out of town."

The bull on the left answered: "You sound sooo tough, I'm shakin' in my hooves. I'll see you in a minute, pretty boy."

This response from the second bull just intensified the rage from the crasher. It was light enough to see, and the bull on my right was the first to break into the meadow. He was all of 300 yards away and perhaps more, but even from here I could see he was a good bull, 4 by 5 and strong bodied. He was everything that he had sounded like he would be—young, on the prod, and full of piss and vinegar. He stood stiff legged and just quivered, watching the other tree line for the bull he knew would come. He screamed one more insult just to make sure. It was something personal like, "Yo mama!" I was sure.

The other bull was in no hurry though. He came steadily on, stopping to grunt and test the wind. He changed directions, quartering the wind and using all the cover he could to approach the coming fun. He was fully engaged for sure, but there was something more. He was smart. By now he had seen the four by five from where he stood in the trees. His deliberate approach continued. It was as if he were letting the bull in the meadow waste his vigor tearing at the ground with his horns.

The second bull was not worried at all. He was like Miamoto Musashi in *The Book of 5 Rings*, preparing for a duel, using every advantage, letting the challenger's anger and cockiness distract him from the real purpose at hand. I had not seen the second bull, but at that moment

I knew he would be victorious. And I knew something else—he would be huge.

That was my second mistake. I was like the first bull. I let my inexperience and peripheral interest in the duel distract me completely from my purpose. The second bull entered the meadow. My mouth went dry. He was the biggest elk I had ever seen, even in pictures. His seven by seven rack was as massive as it was long. The main beams were bigger around than my arm. His horns were the black color of a deep timber bull—white showing only at the tip of each point. He was one-third bigger than the bull I had killed the year before, the bull everyone had said was a monster—my Boone and Crocket trophy book baby. If killing the bull last year had made me a hunter, following that up with this monster would make me a legend.

As visions of the Hunting Hall of Fame danced in my head, the smaller bull trotted across the meadow, away from where the monster had emerged from the trees. He was no longer eager to fight, no longer distracted. In comparing my distraction with his, the comparison ends here. His next act distinguished him as significantly smarter than me. He took a long admiring look at the bigger bull, turned, and loped into the trees. He evaluated the situation and, without guilt or shame, left the country.

The big bull slowly walked to the wallow, took a long relaxing moment of triumph, and then rolled in it. After declaring victory and marking his claim on the water hole and all the cows that came there to drink, he turned and slowly walked across the remainder of the meadow and followed the trail the other had taken. He was smart enough not to leave the same way he had come. What he didn't know was that he had a future hunting legend hot on his trail. He was moving slowly, wind in his face. I would catch him before he bedded for the day. I saw him two more times—both only glimpses and far off.

Two hours later, here I sat. The elk had neatly given me the slip somewhere along the way, and I was very lost and very afraid. I had made two mistakes I had known better than to make. I was in real trouble. I could hear Joseph's words as I considered the hours just passed, "When a child, or anyone for that matter, makes a mistake because they don't know better, that is ignorance and must be forgiven by others and self. When we knowingly choose to do the wrong thing—that is stupid. When we compound our mistakes by trying to avoid the consequences of our actions, we not only just postpone paying the bill, but we also incur interest."

So, that was what I was doing now—recognizing a situation of my own making and seeing what could be done to salvage it before the heavy interest started to accrue. What had Joseph told me to do?

"Don't forget your map and compass, and don't forget to be aware of all around you. Make sure to stop from time to time to look back the way you have come to get your bearings. It looks different from the other direction, but finding your way requires remembering where you have been."

Well, too late for that advice to be helpful, but from here on I would be more aware of my environment. We had gone through the checklist of what to do if lost or separated many times. I did so now, carefully and very seriously. One night at the cabin, while talking with

Gordon Paints His Horses, Gordon had said, "Most people worry about food too much if they are lost. This is the wrong thing. Everybody thinks they need to be Ewell Gibbons, the 'eat-a-plant' white guy. Wants and needs can confuse us. Most of us could live 30 days without food and several days without water. If it is cold or wet, we can die from exposure overnight. Shelter and warmth is what you need first: lack of food and water can make you uncomfortable; lack of heat will kill you. You must always evaluate the difference between want and need."

I would make sure I had a sheltered place before nightfall.

If separated from Joseph, I was to return to a prearranged place, in this case, the truck. If lost, that was not practical. If hurt, I was to make a fire and signal if I could, but I was not hurt. In a situation like this one, I was to go carefully downhill on the nearest game trail. That would most likely take me to water. If it was running water, I was to follow it, not right at its edge where it might wander and be brushy and wet, but, along the game trail that would invariably parallel it at the tree line or the base of the hill. I should follow the water until it met bigger water, making sure I went slowly and carefully and stopped early enough each day to ensure good shelter and fuel to make a fire for the night. If I just did this, Joseph said, I would probably be rescued before I hit New Orleans. If not, and I got to salt water, I had gone too far and should just shoot myself for missing St. Louis.

I checked and inventoried my pack, then started down the deer trail that ran toward the creek I could see below. I found a good protected campsite, stopped my trek before it got too dark, and gathered wood enough for the night. I slept quite comfortably against the exposed root ball of a blown-down tree. The ground tilted in such a way that my fire's heat was reflected into the small hollow where I made my bed . . . Thank you, Joseph and Gordon. I ate some trail mix and heated freeze-dried soup in the tin cup I carried.

The next day at about four in the afternoon, at the confluence of the stream I followed and another slightly larger creek, I walked into the camp of Joseph Thunderbull. He was sitting, his back against a tree, reading a book. He stood, smiled, walked over hugged me, then handed me my belt pouch with compass and maps from my truck.

"It's good to see you," he said, and told me to sit down. He brought me some steaming venison stew from the fire. For about a half hour he read as I ate.

Finally he said, "This drainage is taking you away from the truck, but you did right. I could have picked you up in three or four days at the freeway bridge, but we have one small problem. By tonight it could be 30° below. That would freeze your nose hairs, son, and I didn't feel like waiting till spring to find you and get my rifle back." That was all. Joseph's comment let me know two very important things: first, my stupidity could have killed me, and second, he had saved my life.

He was camped at the base of a big mountain. Farther up the mountain was a sacred place. It was a cave used often over the years by Joseph's family when trapping or just spending time in the mountains. We would go there, he said.

As predicted, that night the weather turned cold. We spent the next five days in the cave on that mountain, waiting out the first northern of the season. It was a month early at least, and bitter cold beyond belief. When I asked Joseph how he knew it was coming, he answered in his best stoic Indian voice, "National Weather Service."

The place was more than just a cave, and very comfortable. It had a plank door and wood stove, with plenty of firewood for heat and cooking, and kerosene for the lamps. He kept a good supply of canned goods in a root cellar, along with freeze-dried food, and, given the fact that this was Joseph's place, I was not surprised to see several shelves of books.

Looking back, what followed were five of the best days of my life. I was alive, we were safe against the storm, and Joseph felt like talking. He never did ask how I had lost my way, although I told him on the third day when my shame had sufficiently subsided. His only comment was typical: "I wish I had seen such a bull."

Chapter Six

The Cave

Receive with grace and dignity.

The Stillwater Buckskin

During the storm he told me about his grandfather's people and about the cave. It had always been there when The People needed a resting and teaching place. He mentioned his father and mother, his sister, her husband, and their sons. He told me for the first time about the wreck that had claimed his wife and young son. This was a holy place I knew, and what was said here was sacred. I was honored to be trusted in this way.

It was here that his grandfather had taught him about the purpose of life. Here Joseph had learned how, why, and where the animals moved. The cave faced east and the overhead that protected the wood pile outside the door made a serviceable porch in the summer. Joseph said this was the place where, over the course of two summers, Kicking Bird had given Joseph his wisdom. His light, or wisdom, was passed to Joseph verbally, and Joseph wrote his words as carefully as he could on a white doe skin. The Stillwater Buckskin, as Joseph called it, was one of his two most prized possessions. The other was the medicine bag his grandmother had given him. He told me he had copied the words of the Buckskin to paper so it was easy to carry. He had read the wisdom every day since his grandfather had given it to him. The buckskin itself was hidden in a safe place to protect it. He had copied it many times over the years as the paper he wrote it on wore out from use.

In this sacred cave, Joseph had made his first bow. He told me about it and about his grandfather, Kicking Bird, as we sat.

" 'When our fathers and mothers worked at making something they sang to it,' my grandfather Kicking Bird taught. 'They sang a song to tell the thing they were making what its purpose was. This is the way the thing they were making first learned of how it should be. These songs or blessings did something more,' he told me. 'They reminded the worker, builder, craftsman, artist, and teacher of his or her purpose as well. Every thing we do when we are building should help what we are making be better. That is why we sing,' he said, 'To remember what we are doing and why, and to teach what we are making its purpose.'

"The first song Kicking Bird taught me was the arrow song," Joseph reminisced. "We sang it together as we selected the material that would become arrows. We sang the same song later as we fashioned the wood we had chosen into shafts and fletched them with eagle or turkey feathers. By that time of course we all had guns, but my grandfather knew we had to buy the guns and ammunition. He told me that until I knew the songs for the making of guns and bullets well enough to teach him, he would teach me. He also told me that until I had the skills to make perfect arrows, I would not know what I had to know in order to make a bow. Without a bow I could not hunt meat. 'How could I be happy,' he had asked, 'if all I could feed my family was fish and roots.' "

Joseph continued, "My father taught me why Grandfather believed making a bow was so important. Making a bow to fit and last teaches you that even though something looks the same as other like objects, that does not make it the same. We must craft every one of our creations to be a reflection of our intended purpose for it. Bows, like our lives, may look very much the same, but each is different. Each is unique to the person who made it. We may all have the same raw material available, but what we select to build with and how carefully we design and fashion it puts our signature on it.

"That is why building a bow is so important to learn—when you are finished, if you have selected and created wisely, you feel strong and able. You know you have the skill to protect and feed yourself and your people. You also have the knowledge to teach others to do the same. That is what a person does. Father said Kicking Bird felt that making a bow the right way taught how to be a good and productive person. It taught the value of satisfaction, of quality and purposeful work. The bow song told me what my grandfather thought was important for me to know. Grandfather knew, my father said, as I sang to the bow to give it purpose, I would learn to listen as life sang its song to me and taught me my purpose. I would learn these truths: gratitude, observation, duty, patience, care, respect, strength, preparation, and many more as I sang."

"Did it work?" I asked Joseph.

"I think so," he said. "I was a typical kid though. The thing I remember most vividly is that Dad told me that until I had made a bow good enough to please Grandfather, I would not get the new Winchester I wanted so badly. That was my real motivation at the time I think, but their plan was a good one. I have used the lessons and skills I learned from making the bow a thousand times. I learned in spite of myself, not because of my good intentions. The proof is in the pudding . . . I have had a dozen guns since then but I still have that bow, and it is still a good bow."

This was the mountain where Joseph's grandfather's father, and his ancestors for as long as memory knew, had been wrapped in soft deer hide and laid to rest. This cave was the preparing place of his family. The truth was found in such places. Every great teacher had experienced the trial and peace of such a place.

Joseph told me that "for Moses, the Bible says, it was the backside of the desert. For Jesus, it was the wilderness. For Buddha, it was by a tree. For Lao-tzu, the misty mountain valleys of the upper Yangtze. For the great swordsman Musashi, it was wandering, sword in hand. Joseph said he had been to many such places. They were everywhere and could always be found if one were looking. Wherever there is peace, there are such places."

"When I was a very young man," Joseph said, "Kicking Bird taught me, 'All you need to know is in the forest if you only watch and listen.' I said, 'How lucky The People were to be the only ones to have the forest.'

"Kicking Bird laughed at this. 'The same truth is in every forest. The store is the forest of the shopkeeper: the same truth is there for all who watch and listen. The sea is the sailor's forest. Life provides both the learning and testing ground we need. Without learning, there could be no testing, and without testing, no learning.'"

As we sat one evening by the fire, Joseph taught me we are all individuals with our own divine purpose. "My grandfather had no Christian name. He was Kicking Bird of The People. There were few enough of The People that every one of them got his own name from God directly. When they were small, their parents would call them some young person's name, like Little Boy, Always Cry, Cub, Pup, or Brown Eyes Shining. Like the white culture, the children of The People are called by descriptive names reserved for children generally, like 'sprout' or 'rugrat.' We could call them sleepers, for example, which means 'the white stuff you get in the corner of your eye after you sleep hard, or when you have a cold.'

"At somewhere between 8 and 14 years old, God sends a message to each child that an adult name is ready for him or her. This is a serious time. The child tells a medicine person, who helps him prepare, by fostering and thinking, to talk to God. Then God gives the child the name and tells him how the person who has that name should be. He tells him who he really is. It is then that child's duty to become the person God told him he really is.

"The People have always had a way to prepare for going into the wilderness to receive the new adult name. When we return, we then tell everyone our new name, and we explain what kind of a person one with such a name should be. In a way, the remainder of our lives is spent trying to be that person. This way we will be who we need to be. When we die, God will recognize us and ask us to come into his house and live. He will say, 'I know you! You are Kicking Bird of The People. You are my friend. Come into my house and rest for a while, then we will build your house in the valley where your people live.'

"When my father was born, he received a Christian name. My grandmother was a Christian woman when he was born, and she gave him the childhood Christian name of Moses. His adult name was Whirlwind Soldier. My childhood Christian name is Joseph," he stated. "My adult name in the traditional way is Thunderbull."

"My son got two names when he was born, in the white man's way. So it is with our crowded world—we share names. This is so we don't run out of names and so we can show honor to our families even if we don't live close enough for everyone to know them. But nothing has changed really. At sometime in our lives, God will speak to us and tell us He has a name for us. If you clean your heart and prepare, you can hear Him tell you your new name. I know you will know it in your heart, no matter how you hear it. With this new name He tells you who you can be, and how you should live to become this person. In your heart these are the things that always feel right to you when you encounter them. There are so many in big cities—you can't tell all the people your new name, and how one with this name should be. I don't know all the rules for each culture and society. I know you can show everyone you meet what kind of person you are, how the person you are should live. I also know this: if, when you die, you have been true to who you are in your heart, God will know you and give you rest and take you to where your people live to build your home."

While we waited out the storm in the cave, Joseph tried knowingly to help me avoid the real danger that was ahead. My getting lost while pursuing the monster bull elk was apparently not the end of my life's challenges, according to Joseph. The danger was obvious to him because of how well he knew me and my choices up to that time. He had told me over and over to remember who God intended me to be. He told me to never forget who I was and what my purpose was for living. That is why every mother and grandmother in every culture tells their young sons and daughters, grandsons and granddaughters, to remember who they are. Great power comes from remembering.

It's like the bow. We sing to it so it will know its purpose. If it forgets, it will lose its spring and be of no use. It may still be very beautiful unstrung and look like the bow you made. However, the purpose of the bow was not to be a decoration. If it has forgotten its purpose, it will have no strength or spring. It will no longer be a bow, no matter what it looks like, and will just sit unusable.

"Do you know why you got lost?" Joseph asked tenderly.

The sting was enough gone that I was able to face the question. "I didn't bring my map and compass from the truck," I said.

"No," said Joseph. "You got lost because of pride. You got lost because you forgot who you really were. Forgetting the map and compass was a simple mistake, the kind we all make every day. There is no shame in being human. You recognized your error in plenty of time to correct it. If you had corrected the error when you recognized it, you would never have become lost."

"But you decided you were above needing a map and compass. You thought you were able to do it all on your own. You felt prepared, you thought you were wise enough, you decided there was no real danger. You may even have gotten away with it this time had it not been for the big bull. But when you saw a trophy that would make you walk taller among your people, you forgot your identity again. Greed blinded you.

"Like the foolish young warriors of another time, you thought only of the glory you would have in battle. You forgot that in battle, some die. It is not just the glory of battle, but the starving winter lodges of The People with no hunters that you must think about before you fight. Our actions always affect others, and you did not think of them, only yourself.

"You have a purpose among men. You have gifts the people you love and serve need. Remember that the knowledge you have comes hand in hand with the responsibility to use it well. When you forget who you are, you forget that purpose. When we become proud, or greedy, or dishonest, we become blinded and foolishly risk what is not ours alone.

"The man who decided after drinking to drive was foolish and proud. He believed he could handle it. He was okay to drive. He was not like all the others who were so much weaker than he. When he died in the accident that followed, he paid the price for his foolish arrogance. My wife and son paid the same price, but for an error they had not made.

"When you saw the bull, you forgot who you were. You wanted the prize without the price. Forgetting the map and compass was not what led you to danger. Wanting the bull was not an evil desire. We all want success. We all are after the fulfillment that comes from accomplishing great things. But we must remember to count the cost before we act.

"Like hunting the bull last year or building the fence, none of us is above preparing before we act. Managing the risk to ourselves and our people is always about remembering who we are and where we fit. Kicking Bird taught me that I belong to all The People, and they belong to me.

"Remember, Bill," and here Joseph looked into my eyes. He peered as intently as I had ever seen. It was as if he were the aging Kicking Bird and I his young grandson, "Before you do anything, count the cost to you and to those whom your actions will affect. Pride, greed, and selfishness will make you forget. We must avoid these blinding drugs most of all if we are to have the medicine to be strong men, if we are to always remember who we are."

I have often thought since how much finer the next years of my life would have been had I really listened with my heart to Joseph that day, if I had learned that day to sing the song of self-remembrance. Unfortunately I did not. His words were spoken kindly, without sting or challenge. I knew he was teaching, and I knew he cared for me. I just didn't realize how much.

When I have thought of Joseph over the years, I have identified him as a man most of all who remembered who he was. It was here he found his strength and power. It came from knowing himself and knowing that being himself was enough. This was what always gave him the confidence to seek wisdom.

Joseph Thunderbull was one of the most educated and well-spoken men I had ever met.

"The power of paying attention" he had said was the origin of his knowledge, but he also had a real flair for the dramatic. The People value great theater and oratory. It was the natural outcome of long, cold winters, and no written language. History, genealogy, entertainment, philosophy, and religion were all passed on orally. He loved to picture himself in the council house, waxing profound and dispensing wisdom with Solomon-like ease. He did not picture himself so out of vanity. To the contrary, it was because he had seen the vision that God had given him of what it meant to be the Thunderbull, and he had accepted both his name and his identity. He really wanted to share. His heart was pure in this thing.

We referred to these moments tongue in cheek as "going Indian." It reminded me later of a young David Carradine in an episodic *Kung Fu* flashback, in the Shou Lin temple learning from the masters: "When you can take the pebble from my hand, Grasshopper, it will be time for you to leave." Joseph pointed out that with the great storytellers, teachers, and shaman it was ever thus. The troubadours of Renaissance Europe, the professors of truth on Mars Hill, the early Moorish masters of Northern Africa and Spain, the wandering monks of China, India, and Japan—all were the same.

"True-hearted people are, and always have been, driven to grow, learn, and search," he mused as we sat by the camp fire. "Few taskmasters are as demanding as our inner drive to learn and teach."

He was "going Indian" at this point, switching into the wisdom-dispensing tradition of his fathers as he continued. I could see him in my mind's eye, fully robed in his finest buckskins, standing tall and proud at the council fire. He was Thunderbull of The People, and he was fulfilling his destiny. I knew in my heart we had gone from lighthearted campfire repartee to something finer, something real. I listened intently.

"My grandfather Kicking Bird told me, as we prepared together for my new name vision, that it was our duty to learn all we could about life, about ourselves, and about others.

"'Why must we do this?' I asked my grandfather. He paused and said, 'When we go to the next world after we die here in this place, we take only two things: what we learn and who we love. That is the purpose of our time here—to learn and love. I am Kicking Bird of The People and cannot lie.'"

Thunderbull's voice shook with fervor and his eyes blazed with clarity and vision, then he bowed his head and turned toward me. When he raised his head, he was once again Joseph—humble, remarkable Joseph—and said, "Only a holy man has the right to end a pronouncement as my grandfather did—by declaring his name, his heritage, and his integrity. He had revealed himself to me, his real self. My grandfather was a holy man, and he had thought me man enough to understand what he was saying and hold that understanding sacred. In teaching me this way, he had recognized me as a man, his equal. I was 13 then, and I have never forgotten that moment and how I felt. That was the first time and one of the very few times in my life I felt really grown up. I have always tried to be the man grandfather knew I could be."

When the weather broke we strapped on snowshoes and hiked to the trucks. It took two days. Three times we crossed the biggest elk tracks Joseph had ever seen. It was nice to know the old boy had weathered the storm.

Two days later, I was back in Communications Theory class discussing "group think" and the Bay of Pigs.

Someone in the Kennedy White House had made a stupid mistake and tried to avoid paying for it. The interest on that mistake was paid in human lives. I decided then and there if I ever realized I had left my map and compass, I would go back for them right away, before I became lost. This proved easier said than done.

My undergraduate education went quickly. It was during my grad school experience that my friend and Joseph's passed away. The warrior Gordon Paints His Horses went to meet his family as they waited for him in the next world.

Chapter Seven

A Time Worth
Not Forgetting

Give without need or expectation.

❁

The Stillwater Buckskin

By the time I got to Gordon's place he had been laid to rest. Joseph along with Sarah's boy Johnson had taken his body to the big mountain where the medicine cave was and laid him somewhere there. Joseph later told me Gordon was wrapped in buckskin and then in one of his beloved green wool army blankets and placed in a safe place where he could see the sun rise. That was all Joseph had said and it was enough.

About an hour after I arrived they returned from the trip to the mountain pulling a horse trailer. They unloaded several riding horses and three pack mules from the back. I pitched in and helped care for the stock before we turned them into the pasture. Joseph threw me a quick nod and went about his duties. It felt as if I had never been gone from this place or Joseph's side. The truth is, with demands of school and a new career, I had not been to the mountains in quite a while. I felt guilty for not keeping in better touch.

My wife, Rebecca, and Sarah were already talking, starting to make up for lost time. The place looked the same as the last time I saw it. Johnson had moved in and looked after the old man for the last year or so. When Joseph had called the last time, about four months before Gordon's death, he had mentioned that his nephew Johnson had been caring for the old warrior. Johnson was a favorite, and he and the old-timer had been close for many years. It was obvious from the condition of the place that Johnson had done a fine job. The yard was clean and the whole outfit was in good shape. It looked like all Gordon's horses were all in the pasture close to the house. I counted about sixty head. They all had been marked by Gordon with the distinctive white designs he loved. Johnson told me later that Gordon had taught him the secret of painting horses, and the two had spent many hours together with the stock.

After the stock was cared for Joseph went to see Sarah and Rebecca. He paid his respects and then came over to me. He said he had missed seeing or hearing from me and was thankful Rebecca had been good enough to write and keep him posted. I had not known she had written and I think he knew it. He thanked me for coming and told me the funeral for Gordon would start the next night. I thought we had missed the funeral and Gordon had been buried. That is when he told me how they had laid Gordon safely on the mountain and returned to celebrate and mourn. This mourning and celebration would begin tomorrow night. We had a service at the church in town the day after Gordon died he said. That was the beginning and seemed to satisfy those who needed to mourn in that way. I asked how Gordon's kids had gotten there so fast for the service.

Joseph said he had called them the week before Gordon died to come and say goodbye. They were already there when the service was held. Before I asked how Joseph knew when Gordon would die, he moved on in his story. He said the service was particularly nice for one of Gordon's daughters and the ranchers' wives who liked church funerals and the lunch and visiting that always followed. "It was a good service," Joseph said. "I'm sure the old man liked it."

He knew of our limited time and had asked Sarah to call so we could come for the mourning and celebration for the family and close friends. "Gordon liked you and asked that we send for you to see how a man is to be remembered." He said Gordon had often commented on how much he wished I would have come to see him. I was again briefly ashamed, but it passed quickly.

Joseph asked me to join him, so we grabbed a couple of fly rods from his truck and walked to the small trout stream beyond the pasture. As we walked Joseph told me what would happen over the next three days.

"We don't have a real tight set of burial rituals in our families," he told me. "What we will do is part wake, part reading of the will, and part farewell. Gordon and I have spoken many times about how he wished to be sent off.

"We will have a sing tomorrow night after we have sweat and cleansed. You may join us if you wish or just watch. It will be much like the preparation we made to hunt the big bull. We will be trying to get close enough to purity for the Creator to hear us as we speak of our friend. The Creator will not hear things that are not pure. The sweating time is also a good time for crying. It is the mourning time when the whole body cries to wash the world from our memory of Gordon.

"When night comes we will sing. Gordon was a warrior and we will talk of his life; some will sing the songs of others who will meet him on the other side. They are doing this for us so we must remember their greatness. Like all of us he kept track of what he learned in life so it could be passed to those who needed it next. Johnson has written it all down to keep, but most of what he left will be sung in the old way for all of us to hear tomorrow night. When the singing is done we will not talk until morning. We will sleep then. When we meet for breakfast we will tell every good story we know of Gordon. Let's catch a mess of fish for that breakfast and talk later." We did just that.

I was up before the light and joined Joseph and the boys for the walk up the hill to build a sweat lodge. The place and materials had been prepared and the day passed quickly. I remembered many things during that good time, and I should have seen my ache and pain coming, but I did not. Joseph led us in singing and prayer. When at the end of our third meditation we dried with sweet grass and cedar and dressed, Joseph put on traditional beaded buckskins. They were not the overly ornamental display regalia buckskins of a fancy dancer, but the carefully prepared simple clothing of a monk. I understood for the first time in that moment my friend was not just a wise man, he was a holy man.

He sang as he finished dressing and carried his medicine bag in full view. I knew he always had it close by but I had never seen him wear it in his belt as he did now. He wore an almost identically sized bag in his other hip. This bag did not have the fringe or beads of the medicine bag but was beautiful in its simple way. As the night went by I discovered this bag contained the sweet herbs and incense powders to sweeten the fire at the singing. Joseph led us back down the hill toward the house. When we arrived it was clear the place had changed and they were waiting for us.

There were 10 or 15 trucks in the yard. A group of wall tents and several traditional tepees had been erected. The family and friends of Gordon Paints His Horses had come to pay their respects. We entered a circle that had been cleared as if for dancing; there was a fire laid in the middle ready to be lit. Joseph sat us next to the fence on the west of the circle facing east and sent a crier to call the wake to order. Everyone was ready of course but respectfully waited to be summoned.

There was a drum to our left and several people seated themselves to drum and sing. The circle formed and Joseph spoke. Rebecca caught my eye and gave me a quick wink. It was clear that she and Sarah were having a great time. Joseph made a short welcome speech and thanked everyone for coming. There were a couple of brief respect songs about Gordon's ancestors, and Joseph laid out the evening. He said we would start with the youngest who wished to speak or sing and would stay until the oldest had spoken. He would then speak last and introduce Johnson, who would share in word and song the wisdom of Gordon Paints His horses. We would quietly think about that wisdom until the morning.

What then transpired is difficult to describe. The life of this good man was saluted in what for want of a better description I would call a series of toasts. These tributes were brief and reflected his character and accomplishments. Everyone who desired rose in order, youngest to oldest and spoke. Many of the older women went out of order in mock youthful vanity and were greeted with good-natured cheers. For example, based on speaking order, Sarah, her silvering hair shining in the firelight, was just under 24. Many, including me, did not speak.

When Joseph rose all was quiet. This moment confirmed again what I had witnessed the first day I saw Joseph and many times since—he was a natural leader. He slowly brought himself to full height and spoke clearly.

"Gordon was a true man. He was my friend and yours. He was a warrior unafraid. He has gone from us to the Creator and his family. He is not gone from our hearts and minds. He chose Johnson Thunderbull to keep his wisdom and to share it with us as we need it. I was chosen to hold the wisdom of my grandfather Kicking Bird, so I know this gift. It is the greatest honor for a man to know from a friend. When a good man gives you his wisdom he gives you his life to hold. He gives you his medicine to be used to lift and teach. I have read the words of my Grandfather every day since I received it. I have tried to be as if Kicking Bird were still here. When I do good it is him you see. Johnson will now know the way to keep Gordon Paints His Horses with us. When you see Johnson doing good, you will now see Gordon as well. It has always been so. May it always be so. In this way each is made better by the other."

Johnson then sang and read the wisdom of Gordon Paints His Horses and pledged to help us keep our friend Gordon alive in our hearts. He would by his actions remind us of his friend and mentor. He ended the recitation of Gordon's wisdom in the traditional way, by announcing his lineage, standing, and intention of honesty: "I am Johnson Thunderbull of The People, a warrior unafraid, and cannot lie."

We slept that night thinking of the old warrior Gordon Paints His Horses, glad part of him was still with us.

The morning brought a fresh feeling to those gathered. The recognized mourning period for Gordon was over, and public remembrances of his life and wisdom would be happy from here on.

Breakfast was a communal feast of pancakes, eggs, potatoes, sausage, bacon, fried brook trout, biscuits and gravy, cheese and fruit, apple pie, lots of juice, and hot coffee—and last but not least was a steaming plate of poached oysters. Everyone spoke of Gordon and reminisced of his humor, courage, skill as a cowboy, and most of all his good heart.

Gordon had left a will of sorts. It was a handwritten note on a yellow legal pad. The instructions left something of sentimental value to everyone there and many who for whatever reason could not be. Johnson and Joseph would make sure all would be delivered. I was surprised to find he had left me an elk tooth necklace in a brown co-op shopping bag. In the bag was a note he had dictated to Johnson saying the teeth would make me a strong hunter. It was to remind me to share my skill and bounty with those who had less.

For the remainder of that day we all spoke and joked of Gordon. Rebecca had received a small war shield from Gordon. Sarah told her it was a great gift to have such protection to cover a heart as tender as hers. It was a tribute from a true friend. We packed and left for home with a real sense of loss. Although Johnson Thunderbull would remind us of the wisdom and character of our friend, Gordon Paints His Horses was gone. With him passed a time worth not forgetting.

Chapter Eight

Lost Again

Even the old snake can teach us.
If we know the teacher is the snake,
learn the lesson by watching
from a distance.
When you have learned,
go far away.

The Stillwater Buckskin

The next years were a blur. We started a family, and I finished my MBA. I also drifted away from my old friend Joseph Thunderbull and what I saw as my childhood. I became less concerned with people. I wasn't even very concerned with continuing my Money 101 studies. After my MBA I had enrolled in a new and I thought far more thrilling and important curriculum. I started with Power and Importance 606, to be followed by Rich and Famous 909.

I was 29, and just where I intended to be. I knew how to play the game. I could move product. I was the youngest sales manager in the history of the firm. My clients loved me, my peers feared me, and everybody knew I was headed for the top. I was a quick study, willing to pay any price to win. I was politically dexterous, shrewd, and smooth—and I was winning.

That year, during the second week of July I received three of the greatest blessings of my life. On Tuesday, my biggest customer, the one I had wined, dined, cultivated, and courted for the last five years, a customer who was 70% of my business, was fired. His demise was due in no small part, it turned out, to not paying enough attention to the needs of his company. Because he paid more attention to the patronage of his suppliers than to his employer, all of the suppliers were to be replaced—with me leading the list.

On Wednesday, I received a call from Emily, the wife of a college friend Paul, the only one I still had contact with in fact. She said my friend had leukemia and was dying and asked if I could help them prepare.

On Thursday, my wife told me she was considering a divorce. She felt alone and needed some time to think and be alone. She was going to her parents' home to work through it.

That Friday evening I sat alone in a darkening house and considered the last four days. My wife had gone. She had taken our young daughter and son. They would spend a week away while we both sorted out our feelings.

My friend Paul had been too sick that Thursday night to do anything but lay quietly as his wife and I spoke about his condition. I had not seen him in several months. He hadn't wanted Emily to ask for my help. She said she had nowhere else to turn and in the end had called in spite of his protests. I was little comfort I'm sure, but I promised to visit on Saturday and begin to help her build a plan for the future. I said nothing about the fact that my own future seemed headed down the toilet—fast.

My boss had called me in that morning and relieved me of my management responsibility so that I might have all the time necessary to replace the sales shortfall caused by the loss of my biggest customer. I was to have a detailed plan on his desk in two weeks to show how I would make up the volume. As I left his office, I knew at a glance my waterloo was not a cause for much mourning among my co-workers; in fact, quite the opposite was evident.

So I sat alone in the dark and empty house, wondering how I could fall so far in four days. I began a tearful and angry, woe-is-me pity party that lasted until about one o'clock in the morning. Anger and frustration finally turned to honesty and fear, and I looked into the mirror and realized two things.

First, I hadn't fallen in four days, but had been falling for quite some time. Second, I hadn't fallen very far because I hadn't been very high in the first place. When all was said and done, I was lost, alone, afraid, and in the dark in more ways than one. I had not taken notice of the landmarks. I was intent on the trophy and had lost my bearings. In my despair, I remembered another such occasion in the mountains of the Stillwater. In that moment I knew exactly what I would do. I was in a hole of my own making and I must stop digging.

I was at the point where I knew I must stop and think and prepare for the sun to come up. If I were lucky enough to live to see it, it would come up as a gift to me. I would be prepared to meet and accept that gift. I would clean my heart, then my mind, and do what mattered most, one thing at a time. I would pray. I would sleep. I would call Joseph Thunderbull.

Joseph's sister, Sarah, sounded well when she answered the phone. She said that it was good to hear my voice and that she wasn't surprised because Joseph had said I would be calling. That surprised me. I hadn't spoken to Joseph for almost a year, since last September when I had called to cancel a hunting trip we had planned. Over the years he had set aside enough resources to leave behind his city house. He was spending most of his time with Sarah and the boys these days. I had been just too swamped to visit. She said Joseph was not there, but he had left a note and said I should come as soon as I wanted. I told her I would start that afternoon and get there sometime on Sunday.

I called my wife and told her I had lost my biggest account, and my position as sales manager. Pride had kept me from admitting this to her before. I apologized. I told her about our friends, Paul and Emily, and said I was spending the bulk of the day with them at the hospital and would do whatever I could to marshal supportive resources for them. Then I told her how sorry I was for failing her—she was, after all, the most important thing in my life. Our family—she and the children, and me— these were my real valuables on this earth. I knew that and realized I had not acted in concert with that belief. I told her that I was going to see Joseph on the Stillwater to clean my mind and heart and that I only hoped that she would have me, the old me, back when I returned.

Her words were loving and kind, and I remember them today as if I were just hearing them. I have always felt that I married way over my head, and no one who knows us both well has ever disagreed.

She said, "Bill, I love you, but I cannot accept us being less than we are capable of being. That is the only problem. We will be glad to have the real you back no matter what happens. Go and be safe; we will be waiting when you get home. I will call Emily at the hospital tomorrow and will follow up on whatever you get done today. Just leave me a note with all the details, and I will handle it as best I can until you come home. There are plenty of career opportunities; whatever you decide, we will be fine. Give my love to Joseph and tell him I miss him."

I called my boss at home and told him I was taking some of the vacation time I had piled up to decide on a plan to go forward. He sounded relieved when he hung up. I packed and then went to the hospital with a grateful heart for my gifts. The sun had come up and I was alive to see it. My wife loved me. I would see my friend Paul at least one more time. I would try and be of some real help to him and Emily. I was on my way to the Stillwater to be an expected and welcome guest of my friend and mentor,

Joseph Thunderbull. I had stopped digging the hole, and it felt right.

I found myself singing behind the wheel of my truck in the middle of the night, in the middle of nowhere, looking forward to seeing Joseph Thunderbull, my true friend and teacher. I pulled over and rolled out my sleeping bag on the foam pad in the back—I was bone tired, body and mind, and could go no further safely. In the morning I would be at Sarah and Joseph's cabin on the Stillwater, and he would help me heal. Then I would get some real rest for the first time in a long while.

I pulled into the yard early Tuesday. Sarah made no comment about my being later than I thought I would be . . . I was here. She walked up and without even a handshake said, "Are you in trouble or sick?"

I said I had been better.

"Joseph said you would be sick in your heart, or you would not come," Sarah said frankly. "He said you were sick when you talked last, but you did not know it yet, and that when you got sick enough you would come for your medicine."

"As always, Joseph was wise," I said. "I have been sick and am here to get better."

"Okay," she said as she turned and went into the house. She came back out almost at once carrying a rifle, a pack, a sleeping bag, and a leather belt with a pouch. I knew at a glance the pouch contained a good compass, maps, and a sharp hunting knife.

"Go to the trail head where you hunted elk that first time. Open the letter in the map pouch, and it will tell you where you are headed. I read it already—you are going to the old cave where Joseph took you that time you went stupid and got lost." She turned, her duty done, and went into the cabin.

I threw the stuff in the back and drove to the trail head. It was only mid-day when I got there, but I knew if the cave were indeed my destination, as Sarah had said, I had at least one night under the stars before I got there, maybe two. It would be worth it. I strapped on the belt and opened the map pouch. There with the maps was a letter. The seal had been broken, a silent testimony of Sarah's admitted trespass.

Chapter Nine

Healing

You must decide each day to be the person
you were made to be and live this way.

You will always know in your heart
how to be this person.

Hear your heart and remember.

❀

The Stillwater Buckskin

The note was clearly from Joseph. It read,

"I'm glad you have come. I'm sorry for your troubles. I have prepared your medicine—it will keep you well from such things as you have just been through. It will be good for you to have such protection in these selfish times.

"Joseph.

"P.S. I have marked the map so you can follow easily. Double-check the pack as Sarah usually steals the candy bars. Hopefully you brought more."

I checked the pack. All was in order, except there were no candy bars. I had brought extras and added those to the pack, along with some fresh food to go with the freeze-dried goods Joseph had put into it. All this left me with three nagging questions: How did he know about my problems? What medicine existed that could heal me every day for the rest of my life? And the most perplexing of all, why was the date on the note November 11th of last year?

I locked the truck, put the keys on top of the right front tire out of sight under the fender, and started the two-day hike to the cave. I fell into the easy rhythm of the hike and began to think of Joseph, my wife and children, Paul and Emily, and just how I had wandered so far from what I really wanted to be.

If you had asked me two weeks before that hike what I valued in my life, I could have, and would have, rattled the list off like some memorized child's prayer. First, of course, my family and those I love; then my health, my career, and my community. These follow-up questions should have been asked: What do you do to show your family they are important? When was the last time you checked on Paul or Emily after you had heard he was sick? How was the hunt last fall with your old brother, Joseph Thunderbull? Do you exercise and watch your diet and stress? How do you provide help or support to co-workers and other company "team" members? When was your last service to the community? Given the answers I would have given to those questions, perhaps it was not so hard to understand how Joseph knew I was sick.

I camped that night in the meadow where I had killed the big bull. I got the hand line out of the pack, caught a couple of grasshoppers, and had brook trout for dinner under the starriest sky I had ever seen. My last thought before sleeping was, "My wife still loves me."

Joseph had taught me to love the morning, and I did for the first morning in a very long time. I was an early riser by habit, often at my desk by 6:30, but somehow I had been missing the joy of it. I had walked right through the dawn each morning and never even seen it. I had missed the pale rose color that announces the birth of every new day, no matter the weather or season.

Joseph had taught me about the sister spirits, one who brings us the day and the other who takes it back home. "Some mornings she lingers," Joseph had said. "Other mornings she just barely brushes your face as she hurries past." Kicking Bird and Moses had taught Joseph to look for her bringing each morning and for her twin sister whose taking of the light brought each night.

"If you learn to know them well," he had said, "You can even smell them as they pass, and they will linger to hear your thanks."

Joseph had learned these things when he was a young boy and told me, "Morning and evening sisters smell just barely like the color of the new dawn, and not quite starlight that accompanied them."

What he taught me of the sisters was hard to describe in words to someone who had not experienced it. But many of The People knew the smell and had often felt their passing. Sarah had said it was like the sweet cookie smell from a newborn baby's soft spot that only the mother and her sisters could really smell. I had learned later in a zoology class that indeed human newborns produce a bonding pheromone that mothers and close female relatives can smell for the first week or so of the baby's life. I had told Sarah about the pheromones. She said she had never heard any moaning, but maybe white women were different.

That morning in the elk kill meadow above the Stillwater, I smelled the morning sister pass, and she lingered just barely long enough to hear my thanks for the day she brought. I would tell Joseph I had felt her pass and remembered to thank her for the day.

As it became light enough to see, the music of the stream and birds accompanied me while I broke camp and started for the cave to meet my friend. The map was well marked and I made good time. I saw lots of deer and twice spotted elk cows and calves bedded down near seeps along the creeks below me. I saw a cow moose in the willows by a big beaver pond about mid-day. She winded me but took no action to avoid my passing.

Sometime later I hunkered down in a stand of quakies and let a late afternoon thunderstorm pass. The lightning struck close enough that it sounded like a bull whip as it came through the air and made my hair stand on end from the static electricity.

Just before dusk I reached the base of the big mountain where the cave was. The rock slides I knew to be ahead would be much too difficult to cross as the light faded. I would camp here in the meadow and go up the mountain first thing in the morning.

Even in July the night air was crisp this high up. It felt good to cuddle into my sleeping bag. I gave thanks for the day and wondered how my family was, and how Paul and Emily were doing; then I slept.

I awoke and broke camp just before dawn, and gave thanks. The sun was coming up, and I was alive to see it. Not wanting to take the time to cook breakfast, I munched on a granola bar and a couple of chocolate squares. This morning I would see Joseph Thunderbull, and my eagerness to greet him was as deep as the sickness that brought me here. With the morning light to guide me, the rock slides provided little delay, and within two hours I was at the door of the sacred cave.

The cave had long been empty by the look and smell of it, and that made me uneasy. Where could Joseph be? He had known I was coming. I left the door open as I entered, and the morning breeze and light began to lift the stale gloom from the room. Nothing had changed much since my last visit almost eight years earlier. I would bet a hundred bucks there was even a fire laid neatly in the stove for an easy emergency start. I looked, and there was.

In the center of the small table was Joseph's tan canvas backpack. Something was very wrong—he wouldn't even go on a day hike without his pack. I picked it up and opened the flap. As always, it was neatly packed: on top was a college theme notebook, hard-covered and cloth tape bound, the kind whose cover looked like fake gray marble. In the box marked "Subject" was a single word. It said, "Bill."

The handwriting was distinctive, the neat printing that of Joseph Thunderbull. He meant the book for me. I opened the cover, sat at the table in the light of the open door, and began to read.

"Good to see you. I knew you would come. I hope it is sooner rather than later. It is the day before Thanksgiving, and I will be dead within a few days. I found out less than three weeks ago I have cancer—very aggressive and very advanced. I'm not in much pain, but I am very weak. Sarah's boys are with me and will bury me here on the mountain. If you wish to know the spot I have asked them to show you. I know you will ask yourself why I didn't call. Two reasons: first, there is nothing you could have done; and second, I needed the time I had left to prepare this pack and your medicine. I knew from your voice the last time we spoke you were very sick, but did not know it yet.

"I hope the hurt that brought awareness of the sickness is not too bad. I have prayed to Father and Mother to make the reminder of who you really are strong enough to wake you but gentle enough not to destroy you. If you are here, they heard my songs.

"Don't mourn for me, my good young brother. My life is full and only my body is sick. I will soon visit Father, and He will take me to Kicking Bird and Grandmother and my wife and son. I hope my father and mother have found their way there too."

I could read no more. My eyes would not drain quickly enough, so I stopped to cry. As I had seen Joseph do, I laid down on the floor with my arms outstretched to show humility and supplication as I prayed and mourned. I expressed my gratitude to the Creator for a friend who had spent his last strength here in this place in the faithful act of preparing to help me heal. It was an hour before I could sit and start reading again.

"In this book are the instructions you must follow to prepare to heal, also a list of the contents of the pack and the purpose of each item. The process to begin will be a familiar one to you: remember the big bull you killed? Sarah would remind you; it was the year before you went stupid and got lost. I love that girl, and she loves you and Rebecca. As my sister, she is your little mother and with my passing belongs to you. Look in on her from time to time and make sure her cable is working. She would die without her soaps and CNN.

"Remember how we removed the man smell from us to hunt the bull? That is what you must do now—remove the smell of the world. We must clean your body, then your mind, and finally your heart. From this time, drink only water and use no spice but salt in your cooking. Go out the front door and follow the ledge to the north for about 200 yards. There is a sweathouse frame there. The firewood is cut and stocked to heat the rocks. The stones are piled there too. Cut fresh boughs to cover the sweathouse frame. Put the woodpile tarp over it all. Scatter dirt on the edges of the tarp to hold it down. Leave an opening on the east side—you can tell where by the frame. Look up, on the peg against the back wall is a buckskin hunting shirt I have made you. Lay it out with clean pants (if you don't have any, wash the ones you are wearing and let them dry by the fire). Cut extra boughs and some sage to rub away the smell of the world. When all is ready, start the fire and heat the rocks. Put a fresh bucket of spring water in the lodge to make steam. After you have placed the heated stones in the pit, shut the tarp, and pour water enough to make a good steam. Sing the songs we sang, if you can remember them, and say the words of your heart.

"If you can't remember the songs I taught you to sing, between the prayer words that come to your mind, just sing whatever. I think heaven just wants to be sure you are happy as you get clean. I might suggest a little Curtis Mayfield, or the 4-Tops, or the Temptations. I have often prayed these songs.

"Leave the sweathouse when you are very wet and getting sleepy. Bathe in the spring (if it is winter, snow will do) and rub yourself dry with cedar or sage. Go back in and stay until you once more break a good sweat. This time just sing. Come out and dry off with sand or dirt. There is some clean sand for this purpose by the wood pile.

"Enter a third time, and say briefly what is in your heart. Come back out and rub with sage to dry. Put on the clean clothes; find a place to sit comfortably, and listen, sipping water as you wait. Father will remind you who you really are, and he will tell you how a son such as you should be. When it is dark, come back here, make some spearmint leaf tea, and read on."

I spent the rest of the day preparing the sweathouse and laying out the cleansing items as instructed. I ate a spare meal spiced only with salt, laid down on the cot, and was soon asleep.

I awoke with the pre-dawn sounds of the birds. I stood and drank cool water while I watched the dawn sister paint the valley. I checked my preparations of the previous day, and then started the big fire that would heat the rocks.

When all was just as Joseph had instructed, I poured the water on the rocks and started to sing. Over the next two hours, I searched my heart for what to pray. Who was I? What did I value? How could I contribute? Why had Joseph and perhaps Paul been taken—while I remained? I thought and prayed these things, singing in between. No matter how hard I tried, I couldn't remember Joseph's prayer songs. Joseph had known I wouldn't, I'm sure. I laughed several times at what someone outside would have thought, as in between silent prayers I expressed my joy in reverential renderings of "People Get Ready," "My Girl," "The Way You Do the Things You Do," "Just My Imagination," "Tears in Heaven," "Runnin' on Faith," and "Maybe I'm Amazed." I considered the addition of Clapton and McCartney to Mayfield, the Tops, and the Tempts to be a meaningful and substantial contribution to my celebratory oratorio. I'm not sure why, but it felt perfect.

After I had dried and dressed carefully, I sat at the edge of the clearing near the spring overlooking the valley, sipped water from time to time, and listened. I had never heard such silence. There was nothing between me and who I was, and it was shattering as I fought the urge to stand and hide. I realized there was nothing between me and who I could be, who I had started out to be, who I wanted to be, and who I really was.

I sat and listened until well after dark. Finally I rose slowly and walked quietly through a most beautiful and peaceful night toward my next assignment. I made spearmint leaf tea and cupped my hands around the warm mug. Then I opened the book marked "Bill," turned the page, and read there a single quotation written carefully in the center of the page:

"All man's miseries derive from not being able to sit quietly in a room alone."   —*Blaise Pascal (1623 – 1662)*

I turned the page and read Joseph's words, "You are tired. Get some sleep, and remember that sitting quietly and honestly with our thoughts teaches us two things: First, who we really are and what we can become, and second, we are not alone. Sleep now. There is a busy day tomorrow. Eat a good breakfast: you will need the brain power."

In the morning I woke and watched the sun rise. I fixed oatmeal with nuts, dried apples, raisins, and brown sugar. It was one of the purest meals I had ever eaten. I went to the book and turned the page: "Knowing what you have been through in the last 24 hours, but not knowing the pain that brought you, I hope you are optimistic this morning. It was my grandfather who taught me the ways of the old people, as he had taught my father. My father was a very good man who was caught between two worlds. He was bright and competent. He made his way in the modern world with ease. He was a superintendent with the railroad. His job took him and my mother all over the West. Mostly Sarah and I stayed with our grandparents. Dad was almost uncomfortable with life here. He commented to me one summer after declining his father's invitation to a sweat and a sing, 'A man who works for the railroad doesn't need that kind of relaxation.' I later thought of the line managers taking a sauna at the club to relax after a long day and realized

Dad never figured out what Grandfather knew: the wisdom that life teaches is available in every forest in the world, even the railroad.

"To my father's credit, he was always proud of his family and appropriately respectful to Kicking Bird and Grandmother. Here is the secret he had missed growing up—being who he was, being true to his heart, was a good choice in any setting. He was Moses Whirlwind, Soldier of The People, of the railroad, of the United States Marines. He was a man true to what he believed and that is enough.

"Kicking Bird said my father was learning this before he died. He was killed trying to break up a knife fight between two young Navajo boys in the rail yard in Gallup, New Mexico. When the train brought his body home, Grandfather and I used the horses to carry it to this mountain ourselves. We wrapped him in buckskin and laid him to rest.

"The reason I'm telling you this is so you will know that the process you are going through is not an Indian process: it is a people process. Wisdom is wisdom, truth is truth. I only know the way I know to give you this wisdom—this medicine—so this is how I give it.

"My father died without preparing me. After my father's death, Kicking Bird brought me here and with some regret did the job my father would have done in old times. Grandfather had me write the process for doing this down, as he was so old and I was so young. 'Perhaps,' he said, 'the words will help you remember if I fall or a horse kicks me, and I die before I can speak the tradition of The People to you.' He not only gave me the wisdom of the Stillwater Buckskin but in the process taught me how to seek and learn.

"I wrote each lesson Grandfather spoke and then we talked of it for a while to make sure I had written the right words. 'The words matter,' Grandfather said. 'The right words at another time will say a different thing. If they are wise words, they will always say a true and good thing. The right medicine words can speak many different truths as the person who hears them needs different things.'

"He told me the magic of words is like the magic of clouds. Two people see a different vision in the same clouds. Maybe because of where they sit, maybe because of who they are. He was not sure how this magic worked, but it does. The right words are magic in this way.

"He taught me that every person must at some time be still to hear true things. 'Learn the value of the fasting, singing, prayer, and sweating rituals to clean body and mind,' he said. 'When you have done these cleaning things and are prepared to hear, sit quietly, and be still.'

"The Stillwater Buckskin is the next thing in the pack. It contains the wisdom of The People in the words of Kicking Bird. I have always called it the Stillwater Buckskin, because it was written in this place. Tonight we will read it together. Until then, you should spend the day preparing the sweat house for the next time it is used—chop wood, replace the tarp, leave the bows from the frame, wash the stones in the spring and restack them, and clean out the pit.

"As you do this, think of yesterday and think of all before who have prepared the world for you. Who built the road, strung the wire, and came up with the vaccine? When you prepare the lodge for the next ceremony, it may not be for yourself. This will help you remember to plant a tree whose shade you will never feel; then you need not be ashamed when you rest in the shade of another man's tree.

"We are all taught by those who have learned before us. We are apprenticed to masters who help us become what we wish to be. It is this sharing that ties us together, beginning to end. This hopeful giving is the unselfish act of contribution we give the coming world."

After preparing the lodge site for its next use, which took most of the day, I went back to the cave and cooked a light evening meal. I sat at the table and read on in Joseph's book. Joseph's note continued, "Below this book in my pack is a white skin tied with a leather lace.

"It is the Stillwater Buckskin—the wisdom of my father's father, Kicking Bird. You have heard the wisdom of it many times though you may not have known it. I copied it to paper and read it every day of my life after he gave it to me. I found it to be true and in concert with the greatest ideas I have ever heard or read. I commend it to you as the wisdom voice of The People. I pass it on to you. Read Kicking Bird's words. You will come to love them.

"This buckskin is one of my two most precious possessions. The other is my magic, my medicine. Mine is with me in the bag as always. I have prepared yours for you. You will find it in a trunk under my bed at Sarah's. For tonight, read the Buckskin. Start for the house in the morning and claim your power to be and stay well.

"Love, Joseph"

Reverently I extracted the precious leather document from my mentor's pack, untied it, and gently unrolled it.

These are the words of the Holy Man Kicking Bird to me, his grandson Joseph Thunderbull, in my 14th year.

Remember who you are...

All The People belong to you, and you belong to all The People. To help them is to help you, and to hurt them is to hurt you.

Where you find good people, stay at that place and be among them.

Some people are bad. They are few but can do much harm. When you find them, go to another place.

Remember humility...

Every day is a fine gift. Speak a grateful word daily to the Creator for such a gift.

Receive with grace and dignity.

Remember learning...

The purpose of this life is to love and learn; this is how you must spend your time.

Observe everything and by observing be taught.

Even the old snake can teach us. If we know the teacher is the snake, learn the lesson by watching from a distance. When you have learned, go far away.

Remember kindness...

Be courteous and peaceful with others and with yourself.

Let other people be who they should be. Even help them in this, if they seek your help.

Give without need or expectation.

Never be cruel or wasteful—even in war. If you must fight, kill fiercely and then go home.

Remember you must choose...

You must decide each day to be the person you were made to be and live this way. You will always know in your heart how to be this person. Hear your heart and remember.

You must choose to be true to what is the right thing to do. Look hard until you find it. Then do this thing.

When you act, don't do many other things inside your mind and heart. If there is something more important to do, stop and do that thing.

Remember peace...

Each day make time to be still and listen.

Do your best and stand quietly: know this is enough for you and the Creator.

This is the true way. I am Kicking Bird of The People and cannot lie.

The writing of this thing has taken two summers. I am Thunderbull.

I would sleep now. In the old trunk under his bed was the medicine he had prepared for me. I left the next morning.

I had the pack from Joseph, and the words of Kicking Bird written on the Stillwater Buckskin. I had fasted and cleaned my heart and mind and taken the time to listen as Joseph had told me. The only thing left was the magic—the medicine bag. I started for the truck the next morning; from there I would go to Sarah's.

After arriving at Sarah's and explaining briefly about Joseph's directions, I went quietly back to Joseph's room. I gently took the buckskin bag from the old trunk where it had been stored beneath Joseph's bed. It was like his in size and workmanship, but different. I loved the smell of it, leather tanned with wood smoke. It was a smell that would always remind me of Joseph. I took it and examined it carefully, excited to know what magic my brother had considered so important for me to have. Here was the thing he promised would make me well every day of my life. There was fringe on two sides and its flap was held closed with a deer horn button. I noticed the objects that had been tied into the fringe as decoration and protection. They were very familiar to me. Some old glass trade beads I had seen many times on the necklace Joseph always wore. There were some elk teeth and cartridge casings that reminded me of our hunting days. There was a tiny coin with a hole drilled in it. It was the widow's mite. There was a key, and as I looked I knew it was the key to a '65 Mustang. This was my bag—it belonged to me as soon as I saw it. It was my medicine, my hope.

I opened the flap and reached inside. To my surprise the bag seemed empty. It contained only a very small pair of dime-store reading glasses. Attached to them was a half sheet of paper, folded small. I recognized Joseph's hand once more and began to read:

"My dear friend, you now have the secret for your healing. What goes in the bag? Only you can know. That is the magic. Place in the bag a reminder of everything you really value. What did you think about as you fasted and cleansed your mind and heart? Take the time to think about what you have been given to love, to understand, to learn, and to share. I shamelessly believed you would want me in the bag and have left you my glasses to remind you of the brother who loves you and was always trying to see the world more clearly. When you have filled the bag with the things you know bring you real joy, look at them carefully. These things will heal you. When the world makes you sick, go to the bag and remind yourself what matters most. Think every day of what is in the bag.

"Then you will know how to use the Stillwater Buckskin from Kicking Bird. Your medicine is strong, as it has always been. The greed and evil in the world you chose caused you to forget what makes you strong and well.

"When you remember, there is no power in this world or the next that can make you alone. There is no bad medicine that can make you weaken and die inside. That is the whole truth in these words from Kicking Bird. When this body dies and we go to the next world, we take with us what we learn and who we love. Put into the bag reminders of what you will take when you go. These things will make you well here and strong there, when we meet again.

"In your heart you will know the way.

"I am Thunderbull of The People and cannot lie."

Chapter Ten

Sharing

Do your best and stand quietly:
know this is enough
for you and the Creator.

The Stillwater Buckskin

The room was quiet as I finished the story. Jane sat quietly for several minutes, then made a final brief notation on her legal pad. She hesitated a second more and began slowly. "That is a powerful story. Thank you for giving me the gift of Joseph Thunderbull.

"Each of us could only hope for such a mentor. Your love and respect for him is evident and well deserved. However, I am left with a dilemma.

"I am inspired and touched; I am reminded and moved to reflection. But am I moved to action? Is the message true? Are we so focused on the money tree that we have forgotten the rest of the forest even exists? Have we forgotten that business and life aren't separate?

"I believe I have. Perhaps even more importantly, I think many people feel the same way. Many of us are like you were. We are lost, and even though most of us remember where we left the map and compass we are reluctant to make the effort to go back and get it. We must do just that and get our bearings before we go further."

As I talked to Jane I shared my belief that "business is a part of life, not the other way around. Corporate integrity is an amalgamation of the character of the people who make up the corporation. Corporate success, corporate wisdom, corporate achievement, and corporate conscience are inseparable from the success, wisdom, achievement, and conscience of the people who are the corporation. We have become so self-centered and greedy that the concepts of personal integrity and corporate conscience seem to be an oxymoron. The problem is not a spreadsheet or system problem, as I had tried to convince myself. It is the problem of abandoned character and accountability. I believe that most of us know that, if we are honest with ourselves."

"As you spoke, the words of great teachers have come back to me with a power I haven't felt in way too long. Jefferson, Donne, Gandhi, Abraham Lincoln, Washington, Adams, Thomas Payne—all moved me in the past and came back as comfortably as old friends when your words called them to mind. Bill, it isn't that I didn't know I had forgotten. I had misplaced the fire of my belief in human nobility. I was afraid to try and find it for fear that I could not. Even if I am strong enough to make the journey, how can I share this in a way that will make it come alive for others?"

"Jane, you will find a way to remind us. Apply the fire you feel to move us to an experiment in personal character.

"The experience and education I received from Joseph, studying and applying the wisdom of Kicking Bird, and searching for the common sense and the uncommon wisdom of great thinkers, has taught me one thing: the principles of success, peace, and happiness are universal and inclusive. We know and embrace them intuitively, when we find them. Add to that the magic of personal motivation taught in the principle of the medicine bag, and you can't be stopped.

"Applying this is about technique, experience, education, and style. Every company, every manager for that matter, has his own way of doing. If what they are doing is based on the kind of wisdom and ethics Joseph taught, they will succeed.

"These principles are the keys to sustainable long-term success. A corporation, a family, or a person that

runs based on them will flourish. Effective management
styles, training techniques, capital processes, and
every other component of competent management are
necessary. However, even the best will fail if they are not
founded on a willingness for everyone to contribute and
a desire for everyone to benefit."

From my drawer I pulled a worn college theme book
and opened it with great care. It was the book Joseph had
left for me so many years ago. I read his words to my
friend Jane:

"'I hope the hurt that brought awareness of the
sickness was not too bad. I have prayed to Father and
Mother to make the reminder of who you really are
strong enough to wake you but gentle enough not to
destroy you. If you are here, they heard my songs.'

"Jane, I have two things for you." I handed her a white
doeskin, tied with a leather lace, upon which I had copied
the words of Kicking Bird. "The original Stillwater
Buckskin is old and worn from much handling so I
copied it for you. Read the words of Kicking Bird every
day, and they will guide you and bring you peace." I then
handed her a small package carefully wrapped in brown
butcher paper. "Inside is a white doeskin medicine bag. I
made it for you in the same style as Joseph's, mine, and
Sarah's. When you have cleansed yourself and prepared
mind and body, sit quietly and listen to what you must
do, then open the package and prepare your medicine as
Joseph taught us. You have the skill, and your medicine
will give you the strength." I read further from the words
of Joseph Thunderbull:

"'You will know how to use the Buckskin from
Kicking Bird. Your medicine is strong as it has always

been. The greed and evil in the world you chose caused you to forget what makes you strong and well.

"'When you remember, there is no power in this world or the next that can make you alone. There is no bad medicine that can make you weaken and die inside. That is the whole truth in these words from Kicking Bird. When this body dies and we go to the next world, we take with us what we have learned and who we love. We take with us our medicine to be strong. Put into the bag reminders of what you will take when you go. These things will make you well here and strong there, when we meet again.

"'In your heart you will know the way.

"'I am Thunderbull of the people and cannot lie.'"

"When this is done, Jane, write the book."

She gathered the precious things from the desktop and paused. Her eyes filled with tears and the words came slowly. "I am going to the ocean to a place our family has gone for years. It is quiet, and I haven't been to a quiet place for way too long. I needed the wisdom of Joseph Thunderbull more than you could know. Before I attempt to write though, I must be sure of one thing. Am I capable of singing the song of its creation as I write it? Do I still know the tune and the words God gave me once, what seems like forever ago? I know the voice that Joseph helped you hear, Bill. I heard it too long ago to be sure it is real anymore. When I clean my mind and heart and listen, will it speak to me still? Will the weight of opportunity lost be too heavy for me to bear?

"I will prepare and I will listen. I just hope I hear what I need to hear to begin again. I believe I was once the person to tell this story. Now I am not sure.

"You said Joseph had given you his trust, and that was a sacred thing and you could not shirk the responsibility of that teaching.

"Thank you for that same gift. If it is possible for me to love and be loved again and to trust and be trustworthy again, I will know it in the stillness that lies ahead. That would the most sacred gift of all.

"I will be back to you when I know if I am the one you and Joseph are looking for."

One week later I received a box from Jane in the mail. I opened it to find a handful of clean white sand and the first draft of chapter 1 . . .

Applying
the Wisdom
of
The Stillwater
Buckskin

Real power can be found in applying the principles taught in the Stillwater Buckskin. Its wisdom will help us no matter where we use it. Though some may try, we can't truly separate who we are at home from who we are at work, or play for that matter—our character is always with us. Those who have passed on to us the wisdom of the Buckskin have made assumptions about our character and quality as individuals. For example, they assumed we—

Know the difference between right and wrong.

Want to do the right thing and will do so if given a chance.

Can be trusted to know if we have made an honest effort in our endeavors.

Are willing to be accountable for our decisions and actions.

Want to learn, to teach, and to be taught.

I believe that these assumptions are valid and that most people will respond to the invitation to apply the principles—at home, work, and play. The secret of great educators and great managers has always been to teach correct principles and then give people an avenue to apply them. Creating a culture and environment that encourages individual growth is the challenge of this book, the challenge of applying the wisdom of the Stillwater Buckskin in the work place and in all aspects of our lives. But to do so, we must have faith in common people, for as Joseph taught, we all belong to each other. We are all common people.

Each person who applies the principles of the Buckskin must begin with some crucial questions: Do

I believe the basic assumptions here? Do I believe in people? Do I believe in my people? Do I believe in myself and my judgment? If the answers are affirmative, the next step is to follow the first basic guideline Joseph gave Bill: Observe, evaluate, act.

"Make it a habit in all you do," he said. "It applies at all times and in all places—before you do anything, learn as much as you can—think about what it is you choose to do. Evaluate what impact your action will have, and then do it. Most people don't have the patience to do all three. Some people want to observe or evaluate it to death and have trouble with the doing, or the finishing. Others simply want to get it done. I guess it hasn't occurred to them to make sure they know what 'It' is and how to 'get it done' before they start doing it. That's why you will see a guy cutting the steel for the same connection three times, because it didn't fit the first two. Remember, Bill, the old wisdom is true that 'it is better to measure twice and cut only once.'"

Another basic guideline from Joseph was to "be willing to be taught." Note what you learn and observe as it happens. We can do this by asking these questions: What is it you want to teach or apply? How will you do it? Let yourself be inspired, and then act.

Bill observed that, "Joseph always carried a short pencil and a small spiral notebook in his shirt pocket for noting what he saw or jotting down a thought. He said getting those small pencils was the only good reason he ever found for golf. No one can remember all the things of value that come and go in a day without writing some notes. Our minds are always working, and there is no telling when it might come up with the solution to a problem you have been considering. Sometimes when you are working or even sleeping your conscious mind gets out of the way and inspiration can happen. When this happens I make a note so I will not lose what I have been given. That way I will have it later when I am able to take the time to consider it. Later after I consider it, I see if there is some way for me to use what I have learned."

Following are some brief reminders of the principles Joseph taught and some thoughts of how you might teach them. They may provide opportunities for you. The list is not intended to be exhaustive but rather as food for thought to help in your process. These suggestions can be used as individual or group activities wherever you find the opportunity to teach. Remember that every situation is unique, so trust yourself to evaluate and apply the concepts you choose to teach in the way that people will respond to them best.

Apprenticeship or Mentoring:

You know you have the skill to protect and feed yourself and your people—now teach others to do the same.

Few taskmasters are as demanding as our inner drive to learn and teach.

When a good man gives you his wisdom he gives you his life to hold, to be used to lift and teach.

In the case of teaching hard and worthwhile lessons to people, timing is everything.

Learning Exercise:

Ask yourself this question: If my son or daughter were coming to work today for the first time, what three things would I hope he or she learned? How would I teach them? Are we teaching these things now? If not, why and how could we teach them?

Planning and Preparation:

Notice how committed the nonplanners are to speed as they run to the gang box four times for tools they should have had. They have confused motion with production.

The miracle of combining preparation and consistent purposeful effort was how much we got done. Joseph taught me how much of success was preparation and planning by showing me.

Planning ahead makes the actual work a game to see if you have built the project in your mind properly.

Observe, plan, and act, before you let your emotions lead you to the nearest lemming-crowded jumping point. Clean your heart and head, and take charge of your direction.

Trying to harvest before you plant is like confusing motion with production. Preparation makes the harvest possible.

Learning Exercise:

List the five most significant challenges or problems you have faced in your business or personal life. Could better planning or preparation have prevented these problems or lessened their impact? Would current processes prevent such events? If not, how could they be changed to protect us?

Producing Quality Product:

Building anything to last and for a good purpose helps build good people. Teaching a person why he is working is as important as how to work.

We built it right, and that is the best signature I can think of.

We may all have the same raw material available, but what we select to build with and how carefully we design and fashion it puts our signature on it.

Learning Exercise:

Ask yourself the following questions: Am I proud of what we do? If it were a work of art would I be proud to sign it? Do our customers get what they expect and deserve? Have we encouraged the proper level of quality in our products and services? This discussion can lead to a clear understanding of what we expect as a company or group and stimulate ideas to maintain or achieve those expectations.

Here are a few more familiar principles from the story to consider along with the others we have mentioned.

Be on time:

"He was always the first one there in the morning. To lay out his day, he said. He loved the feel of being prepared and doing a job right."

Give credit:

"You were good help today, Bill; let me thank you properly."

Be thoughtful:

"I noticed whenever we stopped, Joseph had a small gift to give. We took the time to do some small chore—fix a latch, split or haul some wood, or pull some wire to close a hole in a pasture fence. When it came to those he loved, he held nothing back."

Provide opportunity:

"Just as I suspected," he chuckled. "You're not a rich kid. You're a rich kid's kid. Well, we know who your daddy is, but we don't know who you are. So, let's find out."

Ultimately the best teacher is example. Do we really want to improve? Do we want those around us to grow and develop? We have a responsibility to bless our lives and the lives of others by being true to what we believe is right. That is where we will find peace and lasting personal and corporate success. These two successes are not separate but are extensions of each other. Personal and corporate character are inseperable. No matter what the environment, it is our character that matters.

That is the ancient wisdom of the Stillwater Buckskin.

For further information about how you can apply the wisdom of the Stillwater Buckskin to find personal and professional prosperity, and to purchase additional copies of this book, contact:

Stillwater Associates
P.O. Box 50365
Bellevue, Washington
98015-0365

www.kimanelson.com